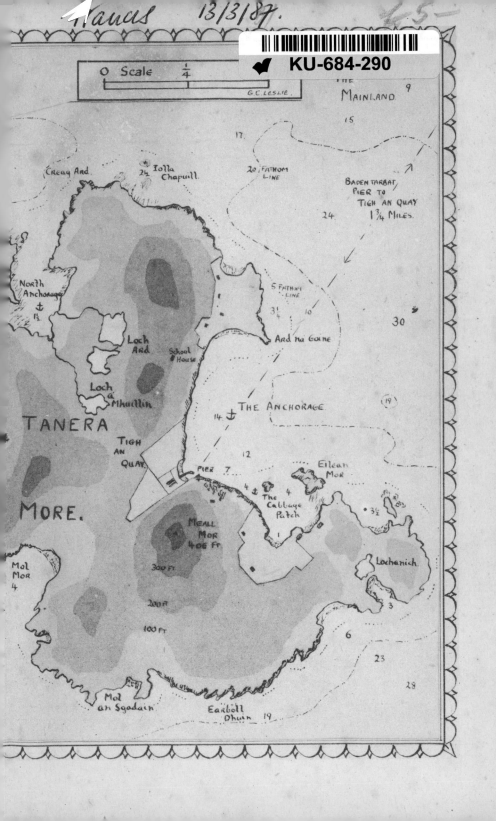

islands 13/3/87.

O Scale ¼

G.C. LESLIE.

THE MAINLAND 9

15

17

20 FATHOM LINE

Creag Ard

Tolla Chapuill 2½

BADEN TARBAT PIER TO TIGH AN QUAY 1¾ MILES.

24

North Anchorage 1¼

5 FATHOM LINE

3¼ 10

30

Ard na Goine

Loch Ard

School House

Loch a Mhuillin

THE ANCHORAGE

14

TANERA

12

(19)

Tigh an Quay

PIER 7

Eilean Mor

4 4

The Cabbage Patch

MORE.

3½

MEALL MOR 406 FT

1

Lochanich

Mol Mor 4

300 FT

200 FT

3

100 FT

6

23

28

Mol an Sgadain

Eanboll Dhuin 19

ISLAND FARM

By the same author

ISLAND YEARS
(*Bell*)

BIRD FLOCKS AND THE BREEDING CYCLE
(*Cambridge University Press*)

A HERD OF RED DEER
(*Oxford University Press*)

A NATURALIST ON RONA
(*Oxford University Press*)

WILD COUNTRY
(*Cambridge University Press*)

THE SEASONS AND THE FARMER
(*Cambridge University Press*)

THE SEASONS AND THE FISHERMAN
(*Cambridge University Press*)

THE STORY OF SCOTLAND
(*Collins*)

WILD LIFE OF BRITAIN
(*Collins*)

THE HARBOUR, TANERA   G.C. Leslie

ISLAND FARM

By

F. FRASER DARLING

D.Sc., F.R.S.E.

Author of " Island Years "

LONDON

G. BELL AND SONS LTD

1944

To

H. E. C. D.

First printed 1943
Reprinted 1944

THIS BOOK IS PRODUCED IN COMPLETE
CONFORMITY WITH THE AUTHORISED
ECONOMY STANDARDS

Printed in Great Britain by T. and A. Constable Ltd.
at the University Press, Edinburgh

PREFACE

THIS is probably the last book I shall write on island life, though it tells only one incomplete chapter of autobiography. An islander should stop writing about isolation in plenty of time or he will find himself in truth isolated from his fellow-men. He becomes some sort of high priest conforming to a ritual devised by a congregation of escapists. There is nothing admirable in escapism. Romance should lead to a positive ideal, not to the oblivion of the lotos-eater, or there will be no romance at all, only disillusion and bitterness. A small island is no place for such people.

This book is part of two people's journey from days of much gaiety and reasonable leisure to a present in which leisure seems immoral. But there are still moments of gaiety which will not be smothered. It has been a shriving experience starting from scratch and reaching a peasant level of comfort in three and a half years. The course was our choice under a certain set of circumstances, for we believed that if our work was to have any value beyond our tiny island world, it was necessary to live the constricted life of labour which is the peasant's lot, just as when we studied the behaviour of the red deer and the Atlantic seals we lived as near their life as we could.

We have reached certain convictions: one is that one family is too small a unit to live alone on a small island. Life is not economical when you have to turn your hand to every kind of job perforce; nor is one family big enough to create and maintain a proper social evolution. Second, there is nothing intrinsic in the peasant life to prevent corporate and cultural development, though in the West Highlands we are indeed approaching social nullity. We want groups of new blood here, groups strong enough to imprint a liberal ethos of their own and yet absorb that which is best in the Gaelic culture. Equally, the Gael would benefit from the leaven and gain a belief in himself which would be expressed by achievement in his own countryside. One of the tasks of the West is to find and raise its own leaders and foster the rare quality of leadership when it appears in the crofting townships.

We began here with faith and still have it, knowing with greater sureness its immense power yoked with hard work and a single mind.

F. F. D.

Isle of Tanera,
Ross and Cromarty,
   July 1943.

CONTENTS

ILLUSTRATIONS

---

*The frontispiece, the end-papers and plate XVII are the work of Lieut.
G. C. Leslie, R.N., and the photographs on plate XIX were taken by
Capt. Ivan Hulburd*

Chapter 1

NOSTALGIA

I WONDER more as I grow older how great is the influence of nostalgia on the course of our daily lives, how far does it make a man creative in the fields of art and action, or does it become his token of defeat? The Scottish people to which the half of me belongs has a traditional nostalgia, and surely in no other race are found at the same time such power for successful action and such nullifying defeatism. Burns Clubs outside Scotland, and the most active ones are outside Scotland, are plain expressions of nostalgia. Elderly men who have left their country gather together to sing the old sweet songs of Border and Island, and it is doubtful if they will ever go back again to stay; they are dead to Scotland, and other countries have reaped the drive of their transplanted will to action.

I also have suffered this sweet and bitter longing and have replied to it by coming back, shedding such worldly comforts as seemed good reasons for not coming. I wanted in those earlier days to live by my science, working as it wished to work, for to me science and art are not far from each other; each is creative and concerned with discovery. Would I work alone, or would I vegetate? Would the West make of me a lotos-eater? Were not the bare attics of Bloomsbury and Montmartre the mills of creative art? I thought of W. H. Hudson's work which I loved so much: was it not all nostalgic writing? Was his work not the reaction to the boundless freedom he had known, a freedom lost when he was cooped in the Bayswater Road? *Green Mansions* was among my six favourite books, for the spirit of Rima was in my heart also and the book spoke direct. Now, I feel that Rima was all in all to Hudson and she is lost in the book because she was lost to him in the almost flesh. Could Rima have lived for us had Hudson not lost his freedom?

There was Fiona Macleod also, that strange figure who lived in several worlds, masculine and feminine, urban and Hebridean,

11

intellectual and primitive. Much of his writing is nostalgic and it cast a spell over me as I emerged from adolescence. He is out of favour among modern Scottish writers, but now, living among the islands as I do and having acquired a stability and sense of proportion I had not in those days, I do not wholly accept their view though I see the faults of his writing clearly enough. Fiona Macleod says somewhere that his picture of the Gael is not a complete one, nor a true one from all aspects. He has taken one facet of the complex Gaelic genius and has exaggerated it, or at least dimmed the others: his critics have it that he thought he was showing the whole man. Sometimes I had to put those books at the back of the shelves, for an essay like *The Mountain Charm* was too strong wine.

These thoughts and many more coursed through my mind as half fears in early days when I had more or less accepted the idea that I ought to be a practical man. But this cloak of practicality never suited me, just as I find it difficult to get real boots and clothes to fit. When I became practical I was dead, and when I was impractical I lived and prospered. The day has come when I have shed the rose-coloured spectacles of my nostalgic longing and the colours of reality have withstood the change. I have come back to a real country where the joys and discomforts of living have given zest to my mind. Now I know that if I am to interpret life in men and animals it must not be from the attic or suburban study, but at the time and from the place where my life is lived.

If I write well enough to please me it is when I write out-of-doors among loved things; and as I write now, in the calm of an October sun, the sea at my feet and the collie lying beside me. The cows are grazing near, the sound of the plucked grass a comfortable undertone in my ears. Sometimes one of them will come across and lick me with her rasp of a tongue—her affection makes bearable the smart. The night watches give me no inspiration to write unless I am outside, and then I can but see and feel the beauty of the night; it is too dark for writing.

I want to recount the growing pains which are not mine alone.

I knew an Irishman once who was farming in Buckingham-shire when I happened to be working in that county in an agricultural advisory post. I was little more than a lad and he was a man of over forty, yet we became friends in that time because we were both like fish out of water. He was longing for the green country of County Clare and the sea mist coming in from the Atlantic, and I was dreaming of the little islands and the same rain-soaked wind from the sea. He could not go back, for he was one of those Anglo-Irish whose house had been burnt over his head and his land confiscated. It was he who introduced me to the delights of Somerville and Ross.

We both loved cattle and horses and would spend hours talking points and pedigrees among his animals, but ever and again this talk of the beasts would bring us to the land on which they fed, and soon it would be the West of Ireland or the Highlands and Islands of Scotland. The older exile was patient with the day-dreaming lad, and the mud, the eternal soul-clogging mud of the Vale of Aylesbury, isolated them.

"If a man has not got where he wishes to be by the time he's forty, he is a failure altogether and he will never be getting there. Do you hear me?"

Indeed I heard him, and his saying has welled into my mind many and many a time in later years as a truth few learn soon enough in their lives. There was another thing he said in that soft voice of his which had yet a strange sharpness and clearness of diction:

"As you stand here, boy, in this sink of mud from which there seems no escape, remember this: if you want to reach your island farm, and you must get there while you're young or never at all, do something towards getting there every day. Never let one day pass but you save a penny or a pound or make yourself abler to live that life."

The Irishman has passed out of my life, but perhaps we met when we needed each other most, and his message has stayed with me through the years. I have tried since to find him, but he is gone and his acres are farmed once more by a man of the Vale who can live in that mud.

There was a time in my stay in Buckinghamshire when I was in danger of not heeding the Irishman's message, but was content to dream nostalgically. I was by this time a factor of an estate and, having come from a harder country, life seemed comfortable and easy. I was sitting in my kitchen one night before a roaring wood fire which made the red tiles of the floor and the brass on the walls a flickering pattern of security, of comfort and of something that was England. England! For me no supercilious and envious Caledonian contempt: I love her dearly. She is my England too. Life seemed good as I sat there in a wheel-backed armchair, tilted gingerly on its two back legs as is my way. Poised there, the tips of my slippered toes lightly touching on the hob, and dreaming into the midst of the burning wood, it was as if a voice spoke in my mind.

"You are wasting your time," it said, "you are twenty-four years old and the girth of your middle will soon be as great as that of your chest. Get up from your dreaming; act; move away from here."

I had been married over two years and our child would soon be born. Surely this was no time for moving. And yet, before the baby was three months old we were in Scotland again, our two or three hundreds of capital providing the means of life while I worked for a Doctorate of Philosophy in animal genetics at the University of Edinburgh.

The doctorate came in two years' time. For me it was a happy time, enjoying to the full and romantically the Edinburgh of my fathers, working on something new with the Mountain Blackface breed of sheep, and travelling the hill districts of Scotland about that work. I was working under a brilliant man who fired my imagination and opened for me new gates of the mind. There was a constant stream of new faces and stimulating personalities.

It was not a happy time for my wife; she saw much more than I did of that Portobello flat with its one virtue of facing the sea. She had all the irksomeness of urban life which we had never known before. The baby was a skinny and nervous creature in the early months of his life; Bobbie devoted herself to him and made him a fine child, and she never let the baby and the work he caused impinge on my life. I think in the interest of my own affairs I grew unduly selfish and got farthest away from Bobbie in that time. She could not walk the Pentlands and Moorfoots with me nor spend the week-end birdwatching in Aberlady Bay.

And yet there was the bond of the island, if a little dim. One day there came someone to call on us; she was a Shetland lady who had been a friend of Bobbie's mother. I loved her straight away, and I know she loved me though she had a grown-up son and daughter of her own. We talked long together of the islands, for the nostalgia was in her also, and she taught me much in the years before she died. Her nephew, Stephen Saxby, came from Unst to study in Edinburgh, and the island bond made us friends. I went to his home in the North Isles for one of the most wonderful months of my life, for it was May and bird time, but Bobbie was back there in the Portobello flat, half living. Each little island we explored I considered as a possible home, though it were bare and far in the sea. They were not all idle thoughts, for I learned things by thinking like that, but I felt all the time it would be in the West I should settle and not in the North.

I learned from the example of Stephen's father the value of a life of service in the islands. He is the Doctor in that farthest north bit of Britain, and I saw the devotion of the people to him and his family. A doctor is a fortunate man because he can minister directly to his fellow-men; a farmer and biologist is in a less good position from that point of view, but I saw in many ways that a man living in remote islands need not bury himself and be lost to the good of his fellows. An island life need be no selfish life.

I was appointed Chief Officer of the Imperial Bureau of Animal Genetics in the autumn of 1930, which meant money coming in instead of the poverty we had endured until then. We moved thankfully to a larger house in Broomieknowe which had an interesting garden and outbuildings. The stage seemed set for a pleasant spell of life, but it was not to be just then, for I suffered a sudden and terrible unhappiness in the loss of a friend, from which it took me a long time to recover. It was now the islands pulled at my heart-strings, and within a month I was walking through Mull and Iona, a very lonely man. An Iona green with spring did much for me then, and a walk through Glen More in the darkness, but my trouble needed time to be healed.

Bobbie worked for my good then as never before, and two

or three friends among whom I worked helped me also. Those
dear folk did what they could and I warmed in their love, but
I knew it must be within myself the battle must be won. When
it was over I found myself in rather an easy world in which
the house at Broomieknowe was the centre. We had our dogs
and I my mice, and we entertained travelling scholars a good
deal. Broomieknowe was full of friendly folk who were
kind to us.

Most days I walked the five miles into the Research Institute
with my dogs alongside me. My room was at the top of the
building, with a circular window facing west, so that the shape
of the Pentlands was my constant companion. Sparrows and
starlings sat on the window-sill and chattered about the life
outside, and over the paddocks below me wheeled flocks of
peewits, crying to me of farther fields. Springtimes were not
easy to bear, though I would rise early and spend an hour or
two before breakfast bird-nesting in Polton Park on the banks
of the Esk. I do not think I tried or knew how at that time to
understand the foibles and mannerisms of the rather artificial
society in which I found myself.

Here was I, a fellow who had overcome much to be a farmer,
living in the country where I belonged, sitting with white hands
in a room in a town. It had all happened imperceptibly, losing
sight of the goal for the sake of expediency. During those years
I had by the merest chance missed going to Labrador to establish
a reindeer-breeding research ranch. That project would not
have killed my island longings but it would have laid them
aside for a while until I had tackled a job close to my heart.
But there, it had not happened as I had hoped, and here I was
getting farther from islands or pioneer work of any kind. Even
the work of collection and collation of scientific literature and
writing summaries of various aspects of animal breeding was
not the pioneer work of science. I began to feel the lack of
discovering for myself, though trying to write a history of
genetical science masked it for a time, until I realized that my
history fell far short of my intentions. It was leading me deeper
and deeper into the dust of the bookshelves and did not com-
pensate for the loss of work with my hands as well as with my
head.

I. LOW TIDE AT TANERA MOR

showing Tigh an Quay, the ruined herring curing station and the quay ; the little
Irish Park is seen behind the ruin

II. TIGH AN QUAY : THE RUIN AND THE RUSHES LOOKING EAST

Holiday times found me disappearing for a week or more into the Cairngorms, to Skye or into the high hills of Appin and Lorne, living hard and uncomfortably, but for the moment joyously. These sallies forth did little more than make me determined to overcome present difficulties and make the Highlands my home. Ever since childhood I had had the power of dissolving into a background of woodland and hill and of becoming at one with the creatures I found there, and now these moments were poignant. It was never difficult for me to stalk deer or to find weasels and hedgehogs whose lives I could watch intently for some short episode; and I have spent hours which were almost mystical in the bed of a woodland beck where the growth of fern and honeysuckle has met above my head, watching the passage of spiders and insects among the liverworts and cross-leaved mossy saxifrage. Tiny silent lives, but not passing unknown.

There was something wrong with my science now; it had lost the simplicity of the wondering child which I think is the approach of the greatest men of science. I did some work on animal behaviour for my own amusement but realized that if it was to be of permanent value and not just anecdotal, I must get away from the artificial atmosphere of experimentation under laboratory conditions, and not place too much weight on what I saw of the natural behaviour of wild creatures in the short periods in which I was able to watch them. I began to see that if I was constructive enough in my thinking, the goal of the island and the life of the man of science need not be incompatible.

At this time I received a gift which brought the island nearer: some old friends gave me £100 to be used for the island when one should come my way. Islands do pass through the estate markets from time to time, but most of them are well-established homes and farms beyond my small means. There was one of 1400 acres which had a good house and natural harbour and carried a stock of Blackface sheep which made me open my eyes, so good were they. The island also carried a big fold of Highland and Galloway cattle. How dearly I would have liked that place at that time, but it was far beyond us, even with the estate market at rock bottom. A good island farm

of 400-1500 acres off the West Highland coast is worth from
£2 to £3 an acre and the stock has to be bought on the top
of that. This particular island was eventually sold for less than
£2 an acre, so low were prices at that time. An uninhabited
and houseless island of 100-300 acres is worth about £1 an
acre, and it was something of this kind we hoped might come
our way. But small properties are not common in the West
Highlands. Small islands belong to large estates, the owners of
which are not generally disposed to part with one small portion
for what is to them an inconsiderable sum. This is only
reasonable.

I remember as a lad thinking I would like the little island
of Inchkenneth, west of Mull. Was this because of its romantic
history as the burial-ground of chiefs and kings, and because
Doctor Johnson was so hospitably entertained there? That
island has had several owners since Sir Harold Boulton, composer
of the *Skye Boat Song*, died. But when I came to know it
I coveted it no longer, for it lies below the great precipices of
Ardmeanach. The south wind comes tumbling down those
1700-foot cliffs, lays flat the corn and rips slates from the buildings
unless they are cemented.

And then, strangely enough, there came into the market a
little island not far from Inchkenneth—Little Colonsay. It was
150 acres in extent and had some sort of a house on it. Bobbie
and I were about to have the first holiday together and alone
for seven years, so we decided we would spend the time walking
through Mull and Ulva and would look at Little Colonsay
on the way.

It was a magnificent holiday: the rain fell at night and we
had fine days of early June sun. We walked down to Cragaig
on the south shore of Ulva to meet John McColum, the lobster-
fisher, who, though now living at Cragaig, had spent most of his
life in the house on Little Colonsay and was generally known as
Johnny Colonsay. He was a fine man to whom I warmed
immediately; his smile was slow to come, his look direct and
his dignity and courtesy would have graced a king. McColum,
and so near Iona: it is a rare name and I have met no other
men spelling it so. John McColum said little enough to us
about the island except that the landing was poor, but he

happened to have with him a garrulous old man dressed in Sabbath blacks. From him we learned that the rats had put Johnny Colonsay out of the island, and a good many more things not likely to give us too rosy an idea before landing. The wind had been fresh before starting and had meant a hard pull out of the landing at Cragaig before John McColum could raise his sail. Then suddenly the boat was a dead thing no longer; she leapt forward, spray flying and gunwale down on the water. John McColum sat silent and unmoving in the stern, one hand on the tiller and the other holding the straining sheet. The two-and-a-half miles over to Little Colonsay, through the skerries and shallow channels that are characteristic of that stretch of coast, were all too short for us. Not only was the sailing stimulating, sea-starved as we were, but John McColum's skill was a thing to watch of itself.

The sun came out as we entered a tiny geo on the north side of Little Colonsay and made us feel more optimistic. It was a good enough landing there today, but it was no place to keep a boat. We said goodbye to John McColum, who was to fetch us the following afternoon.

The island itself was of the same tabular formation as the western side of Mull. The lower plateau immediately above the sea was boggy, and then, set above miniature cliffs, was the higher plateau of good dry grazing. It was up here we met a small herd of wild goats. The house was set to the north-east and had evidently been built with pretensions which somehow had not quite materialized. It had four large rooms with expensive-looking Victorian mouldings round the ceilings. The door had nearly gone; at least, there was room beneath it for a sheep to enter the house. The walls had lost their paper, but in the kitchen, where Johnny Colonsay had evidently lived in bothy fashion, there were newspapers pasted on the walls. These are always readable, and this old copy of *The Oban Times* contained an account of the burning of the MacBrayne steamer in Oban harbour several years ago. Everywhere showed the presence of rats in great numbers—holes in the walls, floorboards gone; the derelict character of the place made Bobbie shudder. I found an abandoned copy of the Bible in Gaelic, and since that day I have come to look upon this battered and

lonely Book as part of the tragedy of a deserted island. In each
such crumbling ruin I have found a copy of the Book : I confess
I have been touched in a way reason cannot justify. Here was
an age-old companion of private hours of devotion, now lying
desperately alone. A worn-out mass of paper and printer's
ink—but a loved book is more than that, and this was a Book
of books.

There was no garden round this house, just a patch of green
rhubarb beside the door.

We put up our little tent outside that night though the wind
and rain would have made the house a welcome shelter : the
rats were too much for us. It was a pleasant enough island we
thought next day as we worked round its shore, climbing
little cliffs and lying in the sun in a tiny bay of shell sand on the
south side, but we were disappointed to find no sea birds nesting.
I think we knew even then that the place would not be ours—
though we might have given our £100 for it had it been
accepted, because nostalgia clouds good judgement. But the
owner lived in southern England and had other ideas of what
an island property of 150 acres was worth, with a house as he
remembered it forty years ago. I remember laughing aloud
when I got back to Edinburgh and saw the agent, who asked
me in what condition were the bathroom and hot-water system.
The only water was a tiny surface well fifty yards from the
house.

Bobbie and I continued our way through Mull, ever reluctant
to be working eastwards to where we should catch the boat.
It was the *Lochinvar* and I found no pleasure in gazing at the
highly coloured exploits of that hero painted on panels in the
saloon aft. There he was on a chestnut horse, the lady pillion,
galloping hard across a bog where any man with feeling for a
horse's legs would have got off himself and walked.

Oban quite depressed us, though it had had power to charm
us even at six o'clock in the morning when we had been starting
our holiday. I felt I could not look out of the window of the
train until we had passed Crianlarich, so bought a copy of *The
Listener* to read. The editorial page bore a long comment on
the institution of the Leverhulme Research Fellowships, which
were to be awarded to senior workers who wished to do a

particular piece of work, but who were normally prevented from doing it by routine duties. I read through the announcement again and showed it to Bobbie.

"I'm going to get one of those," I said.

"You never were blessed with initial modesty, Frank," she answered with a smile that took the sting out of it, and would have dismissed the subject there and then but I said again:

"I'm serious; I tell you one of these Fellowships is going to set us free; it is the rising tide to be taken at the flood."

I thought about it all the way home, allowing myself to look as long as I wanted into the Forest of Blackmount and at the fine cones of Stobinian and Ben More, growing surer of the scheme of research that had lain at the back of my mind for years. How often I had thought that if I could watch a herd of red deer on a Highland hill for every day of a year or more, recording their movements and behaviour and the weather, and trying to take note of as many other environmental factors as possible, then I might have a tale to tell! Here was a beast with a highly developed gregarious habit, a fit subject for sociological studies which might have a value one day for comparison with aspects of human sociology. The reactions of the deer were so sensitive and they themselves so expressive that I felt to watch them would be like watching animal behaviour through a magnifying glass.

When I got home I put the scheme down on paper and it looked good; then I slept on it, re-read, polished and extended it slightly, though paring down words wherever I could to make the short synopsis both precise and concise. Now it looked better still and I was ready to go with it to a friend in the University who might act as a referee. Bobbie was rather nervous about this impulse of mine, suddenly leaving a land of dreams and trying to become real.

"If you don't get this Fellowship and your application becomes known in high places, you'll lose your job," she said.

This was true enough, I thought, especially as I had always shown myself to be of the non-acquiescent type in a job which had all the fetters of the Civil Service about it. I had fought and won a few battles, and was continuing to fight because I felt myself suffering an injustice. That is not a thing to be discussed here, but I had to admit to Bobbie that to let it be known I was eager to leave the job and was positively trying to get out, would be to light a match in an explosive mixture.

"But after all, Bobbie, I'm not going to fail, and I would rather take the bull by the horns anyway."

"Well, if you do, I expect I shall be following you."

My friend in the University, who must be nameless, settled my mind, but with more solid reasons than I had given.

"Apply now, this time," he said in his practical incisive way; "these Fellowships are a new thing and the selection committee have no precedents to govern them in their choice. They come to these very open terms of reference as free men. This scheme of yours is something new and I think they will react to it favourably. I will back you as far as ever I can."

And he did. The application was sent and I put it outside my mind and got on with my job. To think more about it when I had done my best would have been a waste of energy and unfair to those for whom I worked.

I was in Cambridge six weeks later when a telegram came from Bobbie saying I had been awarded a Leverhulme Fellowship. Emotions welled up within me, emotions of relief from nervous tension not admitted, of gratitude, pleasure and anticipation.

The weather that week was all that an English summer could be, with its long days of brilliant sunshine and cool leafiness. I walked along the Backs by the Cam where dwelt the spirit of liberal England; trees, water and fine buildings took on a dream-like quality; then I went into the loveliest building in the world for me and attended Evensong in King's College Chapel. The great organ, the high vaulted roof and impression of space and peace affected me in the same way as when I lay as a child under the foliage on the banks of a woodland burn. I became one with that great place in the chanting of the psalm and came forth humbled. There can be few moments like that in any man's life. And that evening I remember my host filled my cup of joy by playing a long Beethoven sonata on his piano. My sensitiveness was heightened; each bar and chord cut clear into my mind as it had never done before, and I was touched with the inspiration of the master.

The months which followed held much happiness for Bobbie and me though they were not without their trials. Clearing up one life before embarking on another quite different one holds many depressing moments; ties are being broken, ties which we may be glad to break, but which hurt nevertheless when the break comes. There was also the task of preparation. I could not have got a forest in which to work before I was awarded the Fellowship, and I had a good deal of running about before I was entirely satisfied with my terrain. Quartering the forests themselves was sheer joy, but interviews and attempts to get a house were not always pleasant. Three owners of adjacent forests eventually gave me leave to work a piece of country 50,000 acres in extent, which was bounded in such a fashion that I felt fairly sure the deer would stay on the ground throughout the year.

Bobbie and I bought an old car and came north in a snowstorm to look for a house; we had left Broomieknowe before it was light; the Stirling road was a misery of sleet, Drumochter was thick with snow and I had difficulty in keeping the windscreen clear. Glorious, because enthusiasm was driving us forward; and then, when we came to the birch woods before Garve and later to the great pass of the Dirie Mor, the snow hardened and the sun came out to make this one of the best of all worlds, the world of freedom ahead.

We slept in the car that night well wrapped in sleeping-bags and rugs, and the first thing we saw when we woke the following morning was the Brae House, Dundonnell.

"That is exactly the sort of house which has seemed ideal to me," I said. "Wouldn't it be perfect for our job here!"

Strange to relate, it was empty. The floors were rocky and the walls terribly damp, but there it was, the house under the bruach, backed by trees of many kinds and looking across to An Teallach, the highest point in my new territory. By nightfall of that day we had arranged to rent the place, and that is how we came to live in the house from which we watched the deer and in a later time hatched our island ploys. For now I saw that this forest on the north-western seaboard would be the gateway to the islands for us. This life would be part of a training which it was obvious we must undergo before we bought an island for ourselves. I never lost sight of that aspect, and when the island years themselves came, years of living rough and alone, which I have described in an earlier book, there was always the feeling that it was a period of training, a moulding and hardening of character and ability. I know I shall come back again to the subject of learning the job before the end of this book, for island life is in the heart of many folk who have not considered how different it is from the one they are leading. That deep conviction of training for the next stage has been persistent in my mind, and later life has shown it to be true.

Chapter 2

ACQUISITION

I HAVE said that Dundonnell was the gateway to our island life. Those years in the forest brought us to know most of the people living along fifty miles of coastline, and allowed us time to learn the coast itself. Then came the two seasons on Eilean a' Chleirich, the autumn on the Treshnish Isles and the long spell on North Rona. I barely mentioned Tanera in the story of *Island Years* because it had no important place in that book, but it was during those years I first knew Tanera, and it was our coming to Dundonnell in the first place which put the island in our minds.

I well remember the winter dusk of an Edinburgh day when I walked through that part of the New Town where the Writers and Solicitors have their Chambers, to meet the Factor of the Dundonnell Estate and ask permission to work part of the forest. The characteristic little winds came round each corner of George Street, whichever way I was going; Melville on his column was silhouetted against a clear sky, far above the elegant places he thought he adorned in his lifetime, and away to the north beyond half a town was the blue-black ribbon of the Forth spangled with the lights of ships and the little towns of the farther shore. In that air the modern Edinburgh faded, romance was abroad and I slipped back a hundred years and more to the time when my own people had strutted these fine new streets of the Athens of the North—I am sure they would have gilded the lily by using that newly coined sobriquet!

The interview in a room lined with books and a fine collection of Scott portraits and relics did nothing to destroy the illusion, nor did the courtly manners of their owner help to dispel it. The question of a house came up among many others.

"I wish you were interested in a little outlying property of the Estate on the island of Tanera Mor," he was speaking dreamily now, reminiscently; "it abuts the Anchorage and has a pier of its own. I have always had a special liking for that place."

My pulse quickened, but this was not the time for departing from my singleness of purpose, which was to make a good job of the forest and the deer.

"Some other time, perhaps," I said. "I shall not find the fact easy to forget."

Neither did I, for it recurred often enough in the years following. It was a fact few people knew, and I remember the surprise on the face of James Macleod, the proprietor of the rest of the island, when I mentioned Dundonnell and Tigh an Quay in the same breath. This bit of land was a forgotten corner of Scotland, forgotten and, as I found in good time, forlorn.

There came a day in June, 1937, when the sea was so calm that I paddled forth in my canoe from Eilean a' Chleirich, bound for Tanera Mor, six miles away. It was a perfect day and grand going, and in an hour and a half I had rounded the bare, red rocks of Earbull Dhuin, the south end of Tanera, and come into the Anchorage. Here was a different world from the one to which I had been accustomed for many months and which that south coast of the island had led me to expect. There were clumps of rowans and willow trees growing as high as twelve feet, and I was much struck by the unrippled surface of the Anchorage, the shores of which were covered with a heavy growth of knotted wrack, a seaweed which does not thrive on the open, storm-washed cliffs and inlets of Eilean a' Chleirich. I was never more impressed with the sense of haven.

James Macleod's cottage had a small garden in front of it, bounded by young trees which he had planted for cover. My eyes feasted on that garden of flowers for several minutes, on the brightness and gaiety of colour in lupin, primula and many more blooms which are grouped in the mind as old English garden flowers. The bees hummed with a great sound for there were so many of them in such small space. We rowed out to the net slung in the Anchorage and took from it a basket of silvery herring. James Macleod came back to the house immediately to cook some for a meal, but as he left the boat he bent down to give one of the fish to the cat which had come down to the water's edge to meet him.

The meal done, James went to the mainland about his own affairs and I climbed to the highest point of the island to look over the land and sea which here among the Summer Isles made an intricate pattern. It was such a still day that I could hear voices on a yacht coming down Fox Sound well over a mile away. I moved northwards a little from the summit and looked down on Tigh an Quay in the glen, set at the heart of the Anchorage. From four hundred feet above I could see neither the utter desolation nor the true value of the place, but its unique position in such a fine Anchorage attracted me. I decided then I would like to live on Tanera and continue my work from there on birds and seals. The hinterland of islands backing Tanera would be a naturalist's paradise.

Bobbie was eagerly awaiting me when I got back to Eilean a' Chleirich that night. What had I seen, what like was Tanera? I talked long and with enthusiasm for the island. Perhaps James Macleod would let us an empty cottage if we could dig out the earth floor and reline it. There was one among the trees, set with its face to the north, to Suilven and Quinag and the Foinaven group near Cape Wrath. Bobbie went to Tanera another day and liked the feel of the island. She and I let our intuitions have full play in such circumstances as these, for we have found that if the "feel" of an island or house is wrong in the first place it does not come right afterwards. But I had still been no nearer Tigh an Quay than the top of the hill and we did not think about buying it then. Yes, we would come to Tanera, but the time was not yet, and the island had best be put out of our minds entirely until our Treshnish expedition was accomplished. Effort should never be divided.

We went to the Treshnish Isles, lived a new and interesting life with the great Atlantic seals, and came home again to the Brae House. Then began one of those annual journeys to London which are at once a nightmare and a most enjoyable experience. The long journey down in our old car with the snow on hundreds of miles of roads, the series of colds which Bobbie and I always caught on these winter trips and the soft fat we accumulated on our bodies—all these had to be offset against the delight of meeting friends we knew, of good conversation and argument, of good food and wine and many another pleasure. For me also there was the time spent in my mother's house, where I laid aside all the responsibilities of being grown up and became her obedient child again, anticipating Christmas with all the childlike joy that our own son Alasdair was showing.

We returned to the Brae House in March with the southern Christmas fat thick about us. I remember I had called in the Cowcaddens Street in Glasgow on the way down in December to be measured for a new kilt: then I was lean and fit after the Treshnish trip. But when I called to be fitted on the way home the kiltmaker was pained—and I a little shamed.

"Just carry on with the kilt as being for the fellow who came south in December," I said. "I will attend to this chap when I get him home."

The tailor took hold of his lower lip and fidgeted with his tape.

"Do you really think you'll get it down? I think I should slacken her off a bit all round."

"No, no; I'll grind it off with work all right."

Nevertheless, I found a great lot of writing waiting for me at Dundonnell. There was a book to finish and type, some proofs to be read and much correspondence about our forthcoming expedition to North Rona. The wood-cutting with cross-cut saw and seven-pound axe took me a good hour a day, but being a good doer that was only enough to keep me from getting heavier than I was already. The real tribulation of thinning down had to wait until we reached Tanera in the first days of May, 1938.

I happened to be writing to the Factor of Dundonnell in April and the subject of the Tanera property came up again. Bobbie and I thought it over, and on the first good day set forth from Little Loch Broom in the launch we had recently bought for our island work. We went to Tigh an Quay, climbed about the ruin of a house and walked over the sadly neglected ground.

Bobbie agreed with me that if we were not fit and able the place would not be worth thinking of, but we happened to have those gifts. The sense of dereliction and ruin was not enough to take away the feeling that the place and ourselves needed each other. We knew also the queer history of Tigh an Quay, of which I shall write later, but it did not deter us. We came back to James Macleod's cottage then and asked him if he wished to buy Tigh an Quay, because if not, we did. He said no; that he had the rest of the island and the use of the ground meanwhile.

We now had a clear path before us and I wrote to the Factor in Edinburgh in scarcely veiled excitement. A journey down to Glasgow had become necessary for other matters, so I was able to accept an invitation to lunch with the Factor in Edinburgh. He and his junior partner and I went to his club and talked of birds and seals during the meal; the Factor had been on an expedition to Spitsbergen with Scottish geographers and scientists of an earlier generation, whose names were well known to me.

The business of stating and accepting a price for Tigh an Quay was a matter of but a few moments.

"The place is stated to be ten acres Scots, that is, a little over twelve and a half standard English acres, but I would not be surprised if you found it measure up to more than that. Surveying in the Highlands a hundred and fifty years ago was not very accurate. The place came to Dundonnell by a process of excambion for the salmon-fishing of the Little Gruinard River. I should imagine if you offered the Estate something between sixty and seventy pounds sterling it would be accepted; for it is such an outlying corner."

I said that if he would accept sixty pounds sterling, sharing expenses and giving me absolute rights of ownership, I would give him my word. The Factor turned to his junior partner:

"I think we may say that would be all right, don't you?"

And then the Factor told me a little of the way in which Tigh an Quay had come down in the world from the great days of the herring-fishery in the late eighteenth and early nineteenth century until the present when it lay a gaping ruin.

Thus Frank and Marian Fraser Darling became the superiors *pro indiviso* of "All and Whole that piece of Island Tanera or Taneray lined and marked out opposite the Bay of Taneray . . . being part of the annexed estate of Cromartie lying in the Barony of Coigach, Parish of Lochbroom and County of Cromarty, together with the storehouses and other houses and conveniences built thereon and the quay or pier erected on the shores thereof. . . ."

I could have danced on eggs as I went back to Glasgow that night to tell Bobbie, and James Gilchrist with whom we were staying. Jamie is a sailor born and a man with half a mind to be a farmer. He groaned with envy and looked hard at William Daniell's colour print of "Pier at Tanera, Loch Broom" which I had with me. This print is one of a famous series made by Daniell in 1820, and in composition and colouring one of the best. It shows the whole of the pier and part of the terrace, with herring-smacks both in the harbour and in the Anchorage, and little men in the costumes of the period sit negligently on the parapet, walk along the pier or boil tar over a fire at the foot of the harbour. Jamie was conjuring visions of his own little ship lying alongside the quay and of the pleasant life that goes on round a small harbour where boats are constantly in use. Bobbie and I promised him then that when he and his wife cared to have the place and our boat for a holiday it was theirs for the time being; and all in good time they came for a spell and had it to themselves while we were on North Rona.

I cannot well describe my own feelings that night and shortly afterwards when the deeds were finally transferred. Now, a little while before I was thirty-five, an island property had become a fact, a bare fact in truth, but the place was there and our own. We owned part of one of the British Isles and at least a quarter of a mile of British coastline. Ownership of land in Scotland consists of two parts, the superiority and the *dominium utile*. A superior may sell the *dominium utile* for the full worth of the land and still retain the valuable superiority which gives him the title "of" So-and-so, which means much in Scotland, and the right to charge the owner of the *dominium utile* a feu duty. The superiority of Tigh an Quay is worth £2 10s. a year. This means nothing at all monetarily as long as we continue to live in the place, but had we not had the superiority granted to us we should have had to pay Dundonnell the £2 10s. each year.

But to come back to my feelings: there was this exultation of ownership of land of our very own, won after a period of years of intense longing; and there was a more defensible emotion of gratitude. I have taken the path in life of not accumulating worldly goods, of actually choosing poverty in return for the right to live as I wish. I believe that to take joy in gathering riches is bad and exultation in ownership is bad. Yet here was I exulting, and I asked myself how it squared with my philosophy of life. Land, land; what it has meant to me and my family! A fierce love of land above all other riches, and a pride in the ownership of good animals. I should be just as high-chested about a herd of cattle (if I had bred them myself) as about the land on which they fed. Land and stock are in a category by themselves. All this I feel deeply, but if I consider the subject objectively I cannot defend my feeling. It is primitive and not abreast of man's spiritual development, and yet there is undoubtedly a voice inside me which says, "Never you mind, me lad, it may be primitive, but it's good common sense." The very fact that I love land so dearly is sufficient reason for my renouncing it. I overcame that first exultation very quickly, or perhaps it passed of itself, being mere froth, and Bobbie and I have both been left with the enduring feeling that ownership is really custodianship. I have always said that this should be the attitude to ownership of land, but now I do more than state it academically, I feel it through and through. That custodianship is not merely for Alasdair, whose name is in the deeds as heir to Tigh an Quay, not merely for the British nation, but for posterity. We have become more and more humble in our tiny ownership and are grateful for the chance of work it offers.

As land is held in this country at present I should continue to exercise fully and precisely the rights of ownership because I feel my policy to be constructive and responsible. Nevertheless I would support nationalization of the land of Britain as an advance on private ownership if I had more conviction of the State being a good landlord. There is no better farmed land than some of that which men own outright, and most of the best rural communities are on privately owned estates, but the fact remains that some of the worst-farmed lands and most abject rural communities are also to be found on privately owned estates. Land ownership, particularly if there are tenants, calls for the highest expression of *noblesse oblige* and a full sense of responsibility to those living and those yet to be born. The

Government itself, when nationalization comes about, will have to acquire that good type of pride of ownership and not be merely official. It will need imagination and sympathy, with a power to express the nation's love for the land of Britain. We, the common folk, must build for aye and see to it that the country's land policy shall not be mean in conception nor niggardly in execution. The State is already the most extensive landholder in Scotland, largely because of the Scottish Department of Agriculture's buying of West Highland and Island estates for crofting purposes, but, as I see it at present, that ownership works with all the bleakness of officialdom and there is a laxity of responsibility among the tenants. The Forestry Commission, which is also a considerable State landowner, seems to me more human in administration, and that semi-official body, the National Trust, appears to administer its lands with all the charm of the best type of private ownership. Meanwhile, then, we will fiercely love our few acres and hold them fast for another generation and another age.

A great peroration, indeed, about a wee bit ruin, but it is cared for as much as if it were many times larger, and it is the scene of our work and high enthusiasm. Our task and responsibility are greater for the place having been the ruin it was when we came. The first part of that task is to replace the scene of degradation with greenness and beauty.

III. THE ARCTIC TERN'S ROCK AT THE N.W. END OF TANERA (*see page* 36)

IV*a*. THE RUIN FROM THE QUAY, MAY 1938

IV*b*. WE IMMEDIATELY SAID "WALLED GARDEN" (*see page* 41)

Chapter 3

THE ISLAND

COME with me to Tanera and let us see the island before we look more closely at Tigh an Quay. If you sail north of Skye, beyond Rudh' Re and Greenstone Point you will come upon the last considerable group of islands before reaching Cape Wrath—the Summer Isles.

"Summer Isles," exclaimed Pennant in 1772, "Find ourselves near a considerable number of small isles, with a most dreary appearance, miscalled the Summer Isles."

There are days when the casual visitor would agree with the hyperbolical Pennant: only by living there and seeing the seasons through would you say they were well called the Summer Isles. The name possibly came from their being used by the earlier inhabitants of Coigach for shieling purposes—the cattle and the people would go to the islands for the summer grazing. But the cattle husbandry of the Highlands is more or less dead, and sheep have taken their place, so that now the Summer Isles might be more correctly named the Winter Isles. The weaned lambs of the mainland crofters' flocks are put to the islands in October and brought back in February and early March. Those islands which carry flocks of gulls are the best ones for grazing the weaned lambs or hoggs, because they are greener and their soil has a higher content of lime and phosphates.

No other group of Scottish islands is quite like the Summer Isles; they are very rough and broken, covered with peat rather than soil, except where the red rock itself bursts through the black of winter and the green of summer in numerous cliffs, scarps and slabs. They are on an open seaboard, yet among them may be found quiet unruffled anchorages. How delightful it is after crossing the rough water in a westerly wind from Glas Leac Beag to the north end of Tanera Beag to turn south into the narrow sound between that island and Eilean Fada. The water is flat, yet two or three hundred yards away across the island the roaring sea of the Minch can be heard falling on the bay of big shingle and rattling the boulders up and down. Here in the narrow sound are little red cliffs where rowan trees cling and festoons of fragrant honeysuckle lie over the heather. Sometimes the water is deep beneath us, then it shallows to but a few fathoms and looks pale green, for the floor of the sea is coral sand.

All bird notes are clearly heard in there and are something of a paradox. Against the background of the drums of ocean the loud song of island wrens comes over the quiet water, the thin *pi-i-i-i* of tysties, the skirl of a guillemot, the cooing of eiders and the purity of a thrush's song. The shores and the water between the islands and skerries are full of interest, though the islands themselves have little to offer the explorer. Tanera Beag is unusually rough, and despite its wonderful anchorage is quite unsuitable for human habitation. The only water is a shallow brown lochan on the summit of the island. The outer islands of Eilean Dubh, Carn Iar, Bottle Island and Glas Leac Mor have wild cliff scenery but uninteresting surfaces. None is as interesting as Eilean a' Chleirich, which, as I have said in an earlier book, is an epitome of the West Highland world.

Tanera Mor is the largest of the Summer Isles and the one nearest the mainland; from the Anchorage across to Baden-tarbet Pier is less than two miles. The shape of Tanera was undoubtedly its fortune in early times and may be again if the fishing were to come back. It has a large horseshoe bay on the eastern side and the water is deep close to the shore and free from sunken rocks. Ships of 2000-3000 tons could lie in the Anchorage of Tanera without anxiety. The beak-like point of Ard-na-goine provides effective shelter from the north and Rudha Dubh protects the south, together with two little islands on the south side of the Anchorage. These little islands make another small anchorage of remarkable cosiness for boats up to 25 tons; it is called Garadheancal—the cabbage patch.

The mainland shore opposite Tanera is singularly devoid of safe anchorages and it is a bad shore on which to land at all if there is a south-west wind blowing. It can be imagined how much used the Anchorage of Tanera would be in the days of sailing-boats. Here was one of the safest places on the coast and yet well out to sea. A sailing-ship, for example, would not

welcome a journey up Loch Broom to Ullapool and out again
for the sake of shelter. Ullapool as such did not exist until
1780 or thereabouts, but the Anchorage of Tanera Mor has
been busy for a thousand years. The Vikings called the island
Hawrarymoir—the island of the haven—and it was under this
name it was mentioned in the famous manuscript of Sir Donald
Monro, High Dean of the Isles, in 1549.

I have a fancy myself, it cannot be much more than a fancy
meantime, that the name Tanera is very old, coming from an
old Celtic root and meaning island of fire. My reasons for this
derivation are that the highest point of Tanera, Meall Mor,
406 feet, is one of the most conspicuous landmarks from the
mainland hills, from the Torridonian range to the Foinaven
group east of Cape Wrath. Long before I set foot on Tanera
I had seen Meall Mor from numberless points on the mainland
and had been struck by its prominence.

The brown sails of Viking galleys rounding Rudh' Re,
Point of Stoer or Rudha Mor Coigach could be seen from
Meall Mor, and were a fire lighted there the inhabitants of a
great stretch of coastline would be warned and would have
ample time to retreat into the forests which then backed the
coastal settlements. The peat has been cut away from the
top of the hill, yet it is hardly credible that the inhabitants
would have cut their normal supply of peat from up there when
there were peat-hags in plenty down below.

Tanera itself is an island of many small and very rough hills,
dominated by the dark mass of Meall Mor. The ground looks
black because the heather is dark and poor, much of the top
turf of peat has been skinned for fuel in earlier days, and the
Torridonian rock here is darker and less pleasing than the bright
red faces to be seen on our beloved Eilean a' Chleirich which
lies six miles to the south-west. Tanera has three freshwater
lochans in the northern half of the island, but they are not very
interesting from the faunal point of view. But there is a brackish
loch, Lochanach, at the south end of Tanera which is full of
interest to a naturalist. Its shingle shores alone are the haunt
of redshanks, peewits and ringed plovers, and duck may be seen
there most days.

Cliffs and rocky shores practically surround Tanera. There

is a beach of large smooth boulders on the west side of the island and two small shingle beaches in the Anchorage. A tiny bay on the north side of Ard-na-goine also has a shingle beach of light-coloured stones and is called Mol Bhan—the white shingle bay. The fine cliffs of the western side of Tanera do not hold large breeding flocks of sea birds, only a pair of ravens, a pair of peregrines and a few black guillemots or tysties.

The Anchorage itself is certainly the heart of the island. One of the islands in this large bay has a colony of common gulls and the other a varying colony of Arctic terns. Eiders, mergansers and oystercatchers nest on the islands and about the shore of the Anchorage, so in summer it is a place constantly busy with birds.

Tanera has a tradition of the sea first and foremost, and I think this fact, as much as the physical roughness of the island, accounts for the lack of road or good footpath. There is no road anywhere on the island, and the only footpath passing round the Anchorage is a poor and somewhat perilous affair. It scarcely merits the name of footpath, because it is a succession of steep and boggy places which keep you constantly on the hop. This last phrase has come from me without thinking, but I will let it stand because it fits well with the name of pullets, which was given to the women of Tanera in the old days by the people of the mainland shore. These women were so accustomed to clambering about the island that when they got on to a road their feet were unconsciously lifted much higher than necessary. This footpath traverses cliff edges of real danger, because of the tendency of the peat to slough off, and it would not be possible to wheel a barrow round the Anchorage. Hand-barrows carried by two men were used when necessary, but a boat is the common and obvious means of getting from place to place on the Anchorage shores.

The Anchorage was busy from the end of the fifteenth century onwards when the Loch Broom herring-fishery was well established. In those early days the boats fishing the herring-grounds off the West Coast were Dutch, and it seems it was not until the eighteenth century that the local inhabitants became deep-sea fishermen with the improved tackle brought by the Dutch busses. Tanera Mor must have an extraordinarily

interesting history if only it could be unravelled, but, like much
more of this North-West, there are few records in writing. The
Highlands have no Domesday Book. Tanera became doubly
busy after the '45 Rebellion, when the English-owned companies
were taking an interest in West-Coast herring and exporting
them in large quantities to the West Indies for feeding the slaves
on the plantations.

There were twenty-one families living on the eight hundred
acres of Tanera at that time. They each had a few acres of
cultivated ground near the sea, and the hill ground was grazed
communally. This state of affairs continued into the beginning
of the present century, when a rot set in and family after family
left the island. The great herring-fishery of Loch Broom began
to fail about the middle of the nineteenth century when the
shoals moved away from the area, but the effect on the Tanera
crofters was not immediate. It was Tigh an Quay only that
was dealt a death-blow. The crofters of Tanera were nearly
all fishermen, but they used both great and small lines for
haddock and other white fish, and some went away to the
herring-fishery working from the East Coast. They formed a
contented and thriving community, but as the fishing declined,
the other economic and sociological factors which have broken
the old Highland economy came into play.

The last crofters left Tanera in 1931. They had really no
option but to leave, because they were up against the physical
limitations of living on small islands. I have felt this acutely in
our own island years and have remarked on it in earlier books.
But our lonely life on the islands was not concerned with boats
and the tilling of ground. We took all we needed with us and
paid for it in money. The slender thread of one family on a
remote island was always apparent to us, but the tasks were few
that we were really unable to tackle. Only since we came to
Tigh an Quay has the necessity of man power in island life
struck for us its insistent note. The boats of earlier days were
heavier than now and men were needed to haul them. There
were ways then, as now, of lessening labour in hauling, but
winches, blocks and tackle and so on cost money and islanders
have little actual money. When the male population of an
island falls below a fishing-boat's crew it is as good as dead, for

they all leave together then, being unable to remain alone. Their power to work for export has gone. An island is like a tiny nation; if its imports exceed its exports it is bankrupt. Conditions are different for us; the work of our hands would not have kept us fed and clothed when we first came here, no matter how hard we might have worked; research fellowships acted in effect as subsidies until the war came, but since then we have had to depend wholly on what we could export, and our easiest manufactured commodity is my writing. Were it not for this we should be following the last of the old folk from Tanera—and for similar reasons. But my writing has given us sufficient to put some back into the farm, which, with the labour we have put into it in these years, is approaching the state when it will be exporting enough of its own produce to give a man and his wife a fair island living.

The slopes surrounding the Anchorage are dotted with ruins of crofts and little houses of a later date, gradually falling into ruin. One house is let by the proprietor as a summer cottage, but it is so rarely occupied that it does little to mitigate the sense of emptiness which the island conveys. Those older folk still alive who lived here in their youth are homesick for Tanera, and I was told of one old lady who, when taken to the mainland many years ago, pined away for love of the island. She used to go each day to Rudha Dunain, look over to Tanera and weep. I heard also of a cow from here which was never cured of attempts to swim back. Our own son Alasdair, whose connection with the place is brief as yet, loves it so passionately that we have some fears for the hurt that might come to him some day if he cannot make his living here as we are managing to do at present. We too love the island and the home we are now making, it is the salt of life to us, but we are not untouched by an atmosphere of gloom which seems to us part of Tigh an Quay. I do not wish to suggest the place is miserable, far from it, but at the back of everything I get a sense of great age, dark things done, and secrets held.

This sense of the feel of places is queer. It hardly bears description in a gathering of intelligent people, but it cannot be disregarded in the Highlands. Explanation should be sought along physical and physiological lines, but the psychological result is nevertheless there to be contended with, and cannot be escaped. The long-gone people of Tanera were apt to get religion as a disease and they were superstitious beyond the level of the Highlands as a whole. I wish I could get a bird's-eye view of the human history and present it as a psychological and sociological study : that is impossible, but from bits of hearsay pieced together imperfectly and perhaps clouded by the stamp of my own mind, I get a picture of a small community at first living a busy life in which they were not isolated from their fellows because of the constant traffic of boats and the work of the fishing. Then this contact with the outer world stops with the divergence of the herring from Loch Broom. The community grows smaller, less thriving, and minds react among themselves, like atoms buffeting each other inside a closed sphere. There are memories of the dark deeds wrought in the island's history, inevitable in a place far from the beaten track of civilization and visited by wild characters from the Vikings onwards. The small community was now truly isolated and would tend to lose stability. An extreme brand of Presbyterianism coupled with deep superstition is a dangerous mixture. The repressive quality of the one on the dynamic potentialities of the other is apt to cause explosions and disintegration. And, as a social unit, the community of Tanera did disintegrate before it was wholly warranted by economic causes.

If there is a touch of gloom about the empty houses of Tanera, there is added the feeling of doom about Tigh an Quay, the incomplete story of which I shall try to tell. Here is a bare description : The place lies at the most westerly point of the Anchorage, where the land is lowest and becomes a shingle beach at the sea's edge. The beach ends abruptly at the south side in a steep bluff and grassy cliff which is really a shoulder of Meall Mor. The southern boundary of Tigh an Quay comes to the very edge of this beach. The ground rises steeply to the north side also to form a hill about a hundred feet high, called Cnoc Ghlas—the green knoll—and it is part of our property. Its three hundred yards of low cliff glow red in the sun beneath the green of the hill, and pockets of soil are held in the cliff, growing a few aspens, dwarf willows and brambles.

Cnoc Ghlas had lost some of its greenness and gone back to

heather over a large part of its area; but there was still a vividly green cap of grass on the top and we by our work have begun to make the whole knoll green again so that now the cap does not stand out in such sharp contrast. The reason for its old-time greenness and the persistence of the cap of short turf is interesting. The knoll was used in long-past days as the place where the nets of the herring-busses were spread to clean and dry. Herring-nets in constant use tend to get slimy with the floating life of the sea, and such a drying-ground is common to most fishing communities. The dried sea slime from each net acted as a small dressing of a manure rich in lime and phosphates, and through the years the knoll would come green without any intentional cultivation.

The southern bluff of the bay forms one side of a tiny harbour; the other is made by a stone quay shaped like an obtuse-angled letter L. This quay is a beautiful piece of work and formed one of the reasons for our buying Tigh an Quay. It is 80 yards long, 5 yards wide, and with a parapet running the whole length of the north side. Great blocks of undressed stone form the seaward side, and smaller but still considerable stones compose the rest. It is all built in dry-stone except the parapet, which had been done with lime mortar.

William Daniell's picture shows the pier in its original good state, and our copy now hangs facing the view it portrays. It is a pleasing thing to have, but the practical value has been great in providing us with a working drawing for our restoration.

The terrace at the head of the pier was called the Planestones, and so we call this flat quadrangle today. William Daniell helps us no more to visualize the buildings bordering the western, southern and northern edge of the Planestones, so we have had to deduce a good deal and have made rather drastic clearance. The house of Tigh an Quay, nearest the Planestones, and the one-time living quarters of the staff, formed a continuous block of three-storeyed buildings 38 yards long and 6 yards wide running south-westwards. Parallel with this range and 6 yards to the south of it, was the factory, equally long and narrow but not so high. The two blocks were joined by high stone walls at the ends—south-west and north-east. This north-eastern wall has a fine archway leading on to the Planestones, looking down the quay and across the Anchorage. It is one of the architectural features of the place, this archway, and it will be integral in our scheme for reconstruction.

When we first came the inside wall of the factory had gone, so as one entered through the archway there appeared a fairly large space as long as the buildings and 12 yards wide, enclosed by high walls. We immediately said "Walled garden", and that terribly ruinous place has kept that name. Since then we have tackled the job of removing the rubble: the wall fell about seventy-five years ago, on the night a child was born in the house across the alleyway.

I often wondered why it should fall, as every other wall has stood magnificently, long after the roofs had gone. Now I know. Our clearance of two or three feet of rubble and earth above the flagging in the walled garden brings us to the foundations of the wall that fell, and we find it must have consisted of a series of five arches, 10 to 12 feet wide, divided by piers of masonry 8 feet by 2 feet 6 inches. The ground floor of the factory, then, must have been more or less open to the alleyway. All the buildings are done in very ill-shaped undressed stone, and it was no mean feat to take the walls so high, using such stuff. The walls were harled afterwards with shell sand and lime mortar. The mortar in all these walls is made of the coral sand from Tanera Beag and hot quicklime. It is good stuff but tends to crumble if it gets wet. Now this long wall of the arches must have placed an immense weight on the few piers, and as they were not made of shaped flat stones it is not surprising that with slight crumbling of the mortar the whole thing fell out suddenly. And there it remained for three-quarters of a century until we came along. All the buildings were slated with blue Ballachulish slate, which is rather thick and rough-edged.

William Daniell's print is charming, but I wish he had gone to the top of the high bluff to the south of the harbour and done another picture from there. He would have been able to give almost an aerial view of pier, Planestones and buildings, and we should have had still further working drawings for reconstruction. The buildings would have appeared white and neat, and beyond them is the Little Irish Park which he would

have shown as a productive garden, for in his letterpress of the
volume of prints he mentions the garden particularly. We
ourselves have been told of the fruit which came out of Tanera,
including apricots grown on a south wall.

There were buildings of nondescript character north and
south of the Planestones, and north of the house itself were
others. When we bought Tigh an Quay all the buildings
except the house were roofless, and that was far from watertight.
In high gales loose slates were regularly flung down and some
were delicately perched on the eaves waiting for the right puff
of wind to tip them over. That roof troubled both Bobbie
and me.

A doorway leads from the south-western wall of these ruined
buildings into a field known as the big park, a field which is
really the floor of the glen formed by the steep face of Meall
Mor to the south and the lesser hills of the island to the north.
There is also rising ground between the head of the big park
and the sea at Moll Mor. A rocky knoll in this field is called
the lazy knoll or Cnoc an-t-Sidhe, which means the fairy knoll.
The name lazy probably comes from the fact that the big park
was regularly dug, but this knoll was too steep and brashy to
be any good, and therefore contributed nothing to the place.
We prefer the alternative name of Cnoc an-t-Sidhe because we
like a fairy knoll, and in our plans for the future it will not be
lazy, for it will grow some furze bushes, a few birches and
rowans and some alpine flowers in the brashy slopes which form
a perfect natural moraine.

The big park takes the water from a large part of the island,
and unless well drained is liable to flooding. A good system
of stone drains exists, but there must be stoppages in it, for the
whole floor of the park had gone back to rushes and sedgy
herbage had crept into the southern slope. We foresaw years
of work here.

There lies between the big park and Cnoc Ghlas a small triangular
half-acre of ground, bounded on its southern side by the Little
Irish Park of an acre or thereabouts which is to the north of the
blocks of buildings. This triangle is a very old burial-ground
which was used until late in the nineteenth century. The graves
are marked by rough unlettered pieces of stone for the most

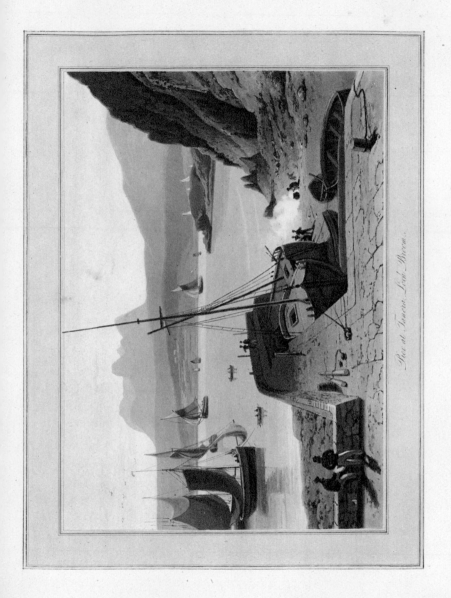

Bois at Tancas, Port Phorim.

part, as was the custom with Highland graves, but the sophistication of the nineteenth century reached this remote place, probably because of the touch with the outside world through the herring traffic. A few flat dressed slabs of ugly grey stone, lettered by a stone-cutter, reached the island at that time. The first roughly inscribed local stone is dated 1790. The serif of the figure 7 has practically disappeared, but the eighteenth-century style of curved strokes is plain to anyone. I have been told in several places, nevertheless, that there is a stone in the burial-ground of Tanera dated 1190! Even without the help of this questionable corroboration, I should judge the place to be a burial-ground of great antiquity because crumbly fragments of human bones crop up in the surface layer of the soil a few yards away. Again, places are few and far between in the West Highlands where you can dig deep enough for burial. I have been told that in olden days people were brought from the mainland to be buried on Tanera; there were several reasons for this, one being the freedom from wild beasts or dogs which tended to dig up mainland graves. And another reason applied to the period when the resurrection men were busy stealing corpses from wherever they could for the anatomists. It so happened that Tanera was not too good from that point of view because of the busy sea traffic a century or two ago. The resurrection rascals came in the boats like sewer rats, and here began one of the tragedies of the island. I have been told that one of these corpse-thieving parties was caught red-handed and the members killed before they could reach the boats.

The burial-ground lay forlorn and desolate, the stones slowly but surely disappearing below the soil. Perhaps it is as well they should go. Our immediate wish was to fence this half-acre, plant trees and shrubs in it and plenty of bulbs, so that it might become a more beautiful place and one more attractive to the birds.

And now for the Little Irish Park, which is one of the gems of the place. Why Irish, you may ask? Again we must look to the herring traffic. Part of the catch cured in Tanera was exported to Ireland and boats came back in ballast with Irish soil. This was dumped and spread in this little field, so that today we have some good deep ground for a garden, and when it was grass it was green the winter through. A good dry-stone dyke all round gives fair shelter, and it is here we hope to grow new things and make experiments as to what can and can not be grown. This little field slopes gently to the south and slightly to the east, so that its lowest part is but a foot or two above the high spring tides which reach the very gate. We want to plan it as a satisfying garden or, as the old word puts it better, a pleasaunce.

There are four old apple trees on the south-western side of the garden, as we will henceforth call it, which are reputed to be 150 years old, and this estimate fits the history of the place as we know it. These apple trees give us immense satisfaction: first, they are real trees, reaching a good ten or twelve feet high; second, their blossom in spring rests our very souls after the wildness of a Highland winter; and third, they bear well. Such apple trees as these would be an affront to any rigidly orthodox gardener. Their trunks are about two feet high and very thick, growing close against the dry-stone dyke. When the branches reach the top of the dyke they turn eastwards, all of them, and the uttermost twigs droop to the ground seven yards from the trunk. It is possible to set a table in summer in the bower made by these old trees, and many are the pleasant meals we have taken there with the willow warblers calling softly in the branches overhead. That orthodox gardener I mentioned might forgive the singular shape of these trees, compelled to adopt it as they have been by the force of two human lifetimes of Atlantic gales. But he would be aghast at the state of the branches, which are matted as close as those of an old wild apple tree. Several visitors have already said to us that these trees would bear pruning. So they would, but they will not get it. The shape of them is dear to us and the shelter they give to the garden east of them would be worth while if we had neither the glory of the blossom nor the abundant crop of apples. The apples themselves are smallish, but the best of them run four to the pound. They are fit for eating from December onwards when they have become a delicate yellow in colour. But their main value is as a cooker: I am one of those who are apt to think plain apple pie rather an anticlimax and that the best part is the crust. Not so with these apples, which have a most delicate flavour when cooked, comparable with that of a berry fruit. The apples do not cook to a froth but remain as tender pieces. They keep until the beginning of June if wrapped in newspaper when picked.

The low walls of a former building remain attached to the main range and jut into the garden; growing within these old walls is a single willow tree which has spread its recumbent trunk in such a way that one tree forms a clump of willows. This is our highest tree, reaching to more than twelve feet from a place the one-time inhabitants used as a midden. The tree was planted long ago to provide withies for lobster creels, a purely practical end. But our eyes see the waving fronds of the willows and how they attract the birds. The desolation of mouldering boots and broken crockery at their foot could be covered with stone; and this we have done.

There was a time when I shunned humanity and cared little whether I had further contact with it; my heart and interest were with birds and beasts. Now it is different; I love my fellow-men, but one of the sins of humanity I find it hardest to forgive and understand is the distinctive capacity for making filth and spoiling what is beautiful. It is not confined to civilized man, though he has many more ways and means of making untidiness than has simple man, and large numbers of people in a confined area create greater evidence of it. But here in the West Highlands where there is so much wildness, an unsophisticated people seems devoid of any wish to dispose of the rubbish which man accumulates. The maxim seems to be that rubbish being rubbish, worthless and non-productive, time and labour must not be spent on removing it from sight. Think of many a township ranged close along the shore and you will remember the amazing crop of old motor tyres, iron bedsteads and broken crockery which litters the shingle. Few houses are nearer the deep sea than Tigh an Quay, yet the generations that lived in it had no thought to take their rubbish far out from shore to drop overboard. Instead, it was chucked into a ruin and left to form a pile. It was just the same when we went to the Brae House of Dundonnell: there was a midden just as far from the door as one could throw an empty bottle—and break it! We cleared it there and made a garden in its place, and here on Tanera we have had to decide whether rubbish should be cleared or covered, for there is a limit to the time we can spend. The midden beneath the willows, then, has been covered.

The walls in which the willows grow have an interest of their own to the naturalist. They lie on the north side of the high range of buildings and therefore get no noonday sun. Tiny ferns and mosses grow there and many of the stones are beautifully lichened. One May day soon after we came to Tigh an Quay, I found a beautiful pyramidal orchis growing on the wall; and when I read about this species in my flower book I learned that it was to be found on dry chalk downs. There are no such places here, but this orchis was growing on the nearest approach to a chalk down—on the top of a wall made with mortar composed of lime and shell sand. This discovery pleased me then and I still think of it with pleasure.

All these damp north walls must have a large population of those primitive insects, the Collembola or springtails, for our commonest birds about the house are wrens and hedgesparrows. The wrens especially are like humming-birds, going up and down the faces of the walls in hovering flight, halting here and there to make closer inspection of a cushion of moss or plant of spleenwort. Centipedes inhabit the lime mortar in great numbers.

A few elders grow in the south-east corner of the garden; they do their best to give shelter and greenness, and they blossom prodigally. So far we have not seen the berries ripen. We have topped and pruned the trees to make them grow thicker, but they have a hard time when the east wind blows after they have broken into leaf. All the prunings have been planted elsewhere, for with us the elder is no weed but the beginning of all-important cover. We have a few chaffinches about the house and garden now and our cultivation has probably induced them to stay and breed, but they have not nested in the elders as one might have expected them to do. I think the reason is that as they are placed at the moment, the trees do not come into leaf from their first shoots of the season but from secondary buds after the east winds have ceased for the summer, and this means that the bushes do not provide the chaffinches with sufficient cover early enough in the year for them to nest in them. By June the elders are full of feeding and resting birds.

Cover, shelter; with these the West can be a kindly country: without them our hands are tied.

Such are the bare lineaments of Tigh an Quay whose "ten acres Scots or thereby" turn out to be over seventeen acres of the standard variety.

Chapter 4

HISTORY AND LEGEND

THE first mention I have managed to find of Tigh an Quay is in the Old Statistical Account. It tells that Tanera, along with the rest of the Cromartie Estate, was then in the hands of the Commission of Annexed Estates, the body which had administered a large number of Highland properties since the fatal year of 1746. Everybody knows that the estates eventually came back to the rightful heirs, but the Commission seems to have made itself rather free of the Highlands while it was in possession. Tigh an Quay is an example, for when the Cromartie lands were restored, this bit of ground of Tanera was not, because the Commission had sold it to a London company of business men who hoped to make profit from the famous Loch Broom herring-fishery.

I have mentioned earlier that this particular fishery had come into prominence in the sixteenth century when the adventurous and industrious Dutch had come to this part of the world in their fishing-busses, with gear far in advance of anything the primitive Scots had developed. The Dutch taught the Highlander how to fish, but from all accounts they received no gratitude, because the Highlanders thought the Dutch were emptying the seas. (That opinion occurs whenever a new or more efficient means of catching fish is used. The Dover fishermen of the fourteenth century petitioned the King to stop the use of the beam trawl which came to be used about that time.)

The herring used to come into the wide mouth of Loch Broom, passing between Tanera and the mainland, going to the head of the Loch nearly twenty miles away, and returning on the other side to pass out to the open sea again by Cailleach Head. This migration occurred with absolute regularity for hundreds of years, and as the fish were present in huge numbers it is no wonder that with the quietening of the Highlands business men should begin to take a hand. Ullapool was built by the British Fishery Society about 1780, the herring being

VI*a*. THE ANCHORAGE OF TANERA

VI*b*. GETTING CORAL SAND TO LIME THE GROUND (*see page* 146)

VIIa. THE SUMMER ISLES, FROM THE MAINLAND TO THE ISLANDS

VIIb. THE SUMMER ISLES, FROM THE ISLANDS TO THE MAINLAND

the town's sole reason for existence. Another herring-station was built in the sheltered east side of Isle Martin, also, I believe, by the British Fishery Society, which got a piece of land along with it from the Cromartie Estate.

Tigh an Quay was bought in 1784 and one Murdoch Morrison, merchant in Stornoway, was installed as manager. There must have been some sort of buildings here then, and probably a small quay, because when we were repairing and rebuilding the quay we found the fabric of a much smaller and lower pier inside the existing one. Presumably, Murdoch Morrison was con-cerned with the building of the extensive ranges of house and factory which make the present ruin. What a fine place it must have been when newly finished!

The change in the migration of the herring made Tigh an Quay a backwater instead of one of the hubs of the Loch Broom fishery. This fact must have reduced the value of the place enormously and one can understand that repairs would not be carried out with regularity. The London company went bank-rupt, there were years of quick changes of ownership, and then a tacksman got the lease of Tanera and Tigh an Quay about 1849. He was a Skyeman called Nicolson, very canny, and out to make money one way or another; he even rented stretches of the foreshore to the crofters for cutting seaware. This was a time when kelp burning was profitable. I have been told that glass was made at Tigh an Quay about the middle of the nineteenth century, but have not been able to confirm this.

Then came a romantic period: the Skyeman had gone and one Captain MacDonald had Tigh an Quay. Stories of this time have come to me from two quite different sources, a Highland lady of my acquaintance and from Murdo Macleod, who was the last crofter-fisherman to leave Tanera. These two met in our house here one summer evening, and I listened to them corroborating each other's memories of what they had been told. Murdo Macleod is well over seventy years old now, still full of interest in old-world affairs. He has the mind and inclinations of an archaeologist, and to him I owe a debt of friendship for many kindnesses, not least for these memories of Tigh an Quay and its neighbourhood. It was he who showed me an ogham stone on Badentarbet beach and the site of the

first church "that was ever in Coigach". And he told me of
MacDonald, a gentleman of the Clanranald family, who loved
the sea and to live outside the law, as well as to maintain his
position as a Highland gentleman. He was known as the Rover
and he had a schooner called *The Rover's Bride*, of which Murdo
Macleod's uncle was skipper.

MacDonald carried on legitimate trade with the help of his
schooner, but he smuggled as well. Now even I, staid and
law-abiding as I am, have played with the idea of smuggling
here. Everything is right: the atmosphere of a private island
stronghold, a good anchorage into which little ships can come
without comment, night-time in which to transfer the stuff
and no one to see, and no customs officer for miles and miles.
Before the war Brittany smacks used to come up the Minch
fishing; no doubt I could have made an arrangement with a
skipper to bring me silks from France, some wine, and perhaps
a few cigars for myself. Silk would demoralize no one, neither
should good wine, and any profits could go to a charity—for,
of course, it would be unpleasant to smuggle for private gain.
It could be done all right, but I am so busy with other things
I am afraid this profitable sideline will have to remain in
abeyance! Captain MacDonald did more than dream, he
smuggled whole-heartedly, apparently making trips to France
himself and sailing through northern British waters for sheer
love of it.

But you get caught some time in the smuggling game, because
you cannot do everything yourself. You share your secret
with someone, and it is only a matter of time before information
leaks out. So with Captain MacDonald; but he enjoyed the
risk, was prepared for it and had a good skipper as well as
himself aboard the schooner. *The Rover's Bride* was lying in
the Anchorage of Tanera one day with a cargo of contraband
when news came that a revenue cutter was in sight. The Rover
weighed anchor immediately and sailed away northwards with
the revenue men hard on his heels. He rounded Cape Wrath
and struck eastwards for the Orkneys, still closely pursued;
the Rover and his skipper knew the cutter was gaining on them,
but neither was seriously troubled if only the islands could be
reached before the cutter drew level. The skipper knew a

passage between two of the islands, through which he doubted whether the revenue men would risk their ship. *The Rover's Bride* went through with every stitch of sail and reached freedom, to return peacefully to Tanera in ballast. It is from this period there has come a legend of a cargo of rum being buried somewhere about the buildings of Tigh an Quay, a legend known as far away as Orkney.

I do not know how the Rover parted with Tigh an Quay, or how the eccentric Meyrick Bankes of Letterewe came into possession of the place. This rich Englishman, a Liverpool merchant, did the most extraordinary things in this countryside and was considered one of the meanest of men. Some remarkable anecdotes of Bankes are recorded in Osgood Mackenzie's *A Hundred Years in the Highlands.* All I know of his association with Tanera is that he used to bring his yacht alongside the quay every year for it to be bottomed and painted. The property came to Dundonnell from Bankes's heirs by an exchange, the other subject being the salmon-fishing of the Little Gruinard River. At this date it seems as if Letterewe got the best of the bargain.

But who knows what may come out of Tigh an Quay one day ? There is another legend of buried treasure on our ground, and Murdo Macleod has shown me the area where it may be found. He says that when he was a lad and this bit of ground was regularly turned with a *cas-chrom* or crooked spade they would sometimes find silver coins about the size of a shilling. I asked him what sort of coins, was there any inscription, date or head in relief ?

"Och, we wouldn't be knowing anything about that," he said ; "there was very little real money about in those days and the coins were nothing to us but curiosities."

Some day before many years have gone by I shall be breaking that ground myself, going deeper than ever the *cas-chrom* dug. There are big boulders in the ground there and I would like them out of the way, because that bit of the big park is sheltered from the east and had the reputation of being good for early potatoes. Perhaps I shall find a silver coin or the hoard from which the early ones came. The value may be negligible in terms of money, but how rich in history and interest ! Remembering the long, unwritten story of Tanera as a haven from Viking days, through the period of the Dutch fishery and the later turbulent history of the Highlands, there is a good chance of treasure being hidden here. Suppose it were a Viking hoard, hastily buried, telling a tale of robberies farther down the coast where the Celtic civilization had reached a high standard, or containing Byzantine coins, which seem to have come to Britain with the Vikings? Or it might be some islander's small savings, buried as they often were in the seventeenth and eighteenth centuries.

Such treasures have been found from time to time in the Highlands, some without the fact being made known. This very one on Tanera may have been lifted long ago and the only treasure I will ever get from that ground will be that of the fable—the good land resulting from deep digging and thorough breaking up of the soil. The Brahan Seer knew of the Tanera treasure, apparently, and foretold it would be found by a one-eyed Macleod. Coigach is full of Macleods, but all those I know have both eyes in their heads as yet.

There is a story current in Coigach of some men gathering sheep on Horse Island, less than two miles from Tanera and closer to the mainland: one of the men fell with one leg deep into a hole in the peat—a very easy and common thing to do— but he got up and ran on after the sheep. That night, two golden guineas fell out of his sock as he kicked off his sea-boots. He quartered the ground thoroughly after that, trying to follow his track exactly, but the story goes that he never found the hole of the golden guineas.

As I say, my friend Murdo Macleod the elder is a man full of old tales. He and his son of the same name bring us a mail once a week and they usually find time for a crack before going back to the mainland. I could see the old man was happy one day, soon after we had reached an advanced stage in rebuilding the quay. He was inspecting the new work, walking the stone flags where lately the sea had covered a litter of fallen stones; and the parapet—such a wall is built along a quay for two reasons, of which that of an additional windbreak is perhaps the lesser! The parapet has the social value of a leaning-place where men in moments of inactivity may place their elbows and gaze across the water. Such a place has an evocative quality, drawing forth reminiscence in a fine reflective style, and tales we had thought forgotten.

"The 'prentice will soon be above MacCrimmon," said my companion.

I looked at him enquiringly for I did not get his meaning, but it was better not to speak.

"I was looking at the boy," he said.

Alasdair was rowing the dinghy about the Anchorage, getting the feel of oars into his hands and making practice approaches to a mooring buoy. Murdo is an accomplished raconteur, a man with the art of a seannachie, and his remarks thus far had made me the eager listener. He reached unhurriedly for his roll of twist and his knife and began paring thinly the tobacco into his palm before continuing in a manner almost deprecatory.

"Och, it was just an old story and a saying they had in the island here."

The knife closed with a snap and was exchanged in his pocket for a pipe, with the stem of which he pointed to the foundations of those rude and ancient dwellings at the sea's edge, under the dyke of the Little Irish Park.

"There were houses there once, though it's not myself that remembers them. In the far one, under the rock, lived a MacCrimmon."

The old man turned to me quickly and his bright blue eyes shone from among the wrinkles and through the haze of new tobacco smoke.

"You'll be thinking that a queer name to be in Tanera, but it was like this: it was that Skyeman called Nicolson, a tacksman he was, who rented the whole of the island from the proprietor; and then he parcelled it out to the crofters and charged very high rents. In this way, d'you see, he was getting the herring-factory and quay for practically nothing at all. It was himself that brought people from Skye for curing the herring, and one of these men was MacCrimmon, who lived yonder with his son, just a young lad of perhaps fourteen or sixteen years old.

"Well now, this MacCrimmon was out on the sea one summer evening and the boy was alone at the house there, practising on the chanter. 'Hidraho, horodo' and so on he was playing to himself, but he wasn't just getting the touch as he would have liked it. And then he was feeling he was not alone, whatever; there was a stranger standing beside him. I'm sure you'll know that when you live on an island you are accustomed to see who will be coming ashore, and to feel a strange man beside you is a queer thing altogether. But this lad wasn't feeling surprised at all, nor when the stranger stood behind him and brought his own fingers on to the boy's as they rested on the chanter, like this, look you.

"'Now then,' says he, 'be trying it again with me.'

"The boy played, and he was finding himself playing as he had never played until then. He was forgetting everything else now and he took out the full pipes. The stranger had disappeared, but the boy, he was hardly noticing that as the bag swelled in his oxter. This was not the chanter any more but the pipes.

"The father of the boy came round Ard-na-goine yonder in the boat and was hearing the pipes over the water. He turned to the other fellow in the boat, very strange like, and he says:

"'The 'prentice is above MacCrimmon.'

"And that was a saying in the island ever since when a lad was getting as good as his father at doing anything."

The old man lifted the cap from his pipe, lit another match and slowly puffed the tobacco to redness. The cap was carefully replaced; blue smoke hung on the air as he turned to me.

"And that boy grew to be a famous piper of the MacCrimmons, but it brought him a lot of envy from others not so good. There came a day when he was to play in a great competition of pipers, and these people knew it was young MacCrimmon would surely be winning it. Those men came in the night to where MacCrimmon was lying asleep and they were sticking needles into the bag of his pipes, making such little holes in it you would never see them.

"And so in the morning, when MacCrimmon came to play before the judges, he was finding it hard to keep the bag full, and as you know, a pibroch takes a long time to play through. But this MacCrimmon, he was a proud lad altogether, and he blew the harder, rather than say there was something wrong with his pipes. He finished his piece, though all was black in front of his eyes, and then—then he spewed up the blood of his heart."

Many other queer things have happened in Tanera. In another of those old black houses near MacCrimmon's there lived a bachelor who was credited with the second sight: it afflicted him in this way—a knock would be heard on his door and he, taking down the bar, would see a cortège passing in the darkness on its way to the burial-ground above the Irish Park. He would see the face of the corpse in this ghostly procession and then knew which of the islanders would be the next to make the journey in reality.

Fiona Macleod must have known Tanera and its strange tales, for in that series of macabre stories grouped in *Under the Dark Star* he tells of the family of Achanna who lived in Eileanmore of the Summer Isles. In the first of these stories, *The Dan nan Ron*, murder is done aboard a fishing-smack in the Anchorage, and the atmosphere of doom and gloom about the place is well described. The Achanna family apparently occupied our property in Fiona Macleod's fancy; the folk seemed cursed and tragedy after tragedy befell them—and prophetically, the ultimate abandonment of the island is mentioned.

But the family that came to Tigh an Quay in 1868 and finally left it in 1923 did suffer dire misfortune. There were two brothers and their wives, industrious folk who dug the whole of the big park—from deck to deck as Murdo Macleod said to me. The wall of the arches fell after they came, when the child was born. What a shock that great fall of masonry just outside the windows must have been to the poor woman, the cracking of joists and roof timbers as the inside came down, and the thin sound of innumerable slates clattering over all! How typical of the West that it lay where it fell for seventy years and more!

Soon after that the death-watch beetle got into the red pine timbering of the house and remaining range of buildings and utterly riddled the place. Floors and roof of the buildings collapsed, so that little more than the house and immediate penthouses remained. When we came to pull the house to bits, very gingerly for fear of it coming down about our ears, we found many of the poor little bodging jobs the occupants had done to maintain the interior structure a little longer. I have heard that towards the end one poor woman went half-way through a floor when carrying a bowl of milk across the room. Incidents like that are upsetting to the nerves.

The last quarter of the nineteenth century must have been rather a nightmare for the people of Tigh an Quay; ruin was growing all about them, ruin of the industry, ruin of the buildings, and the beginnings of ruin of the quay when fishing-smacks from Stornoway brazenly came in one day when all the menfolk were at the fishing, and took away many of the dressed stones which formed the coping of the quay. Once rot has begun in a place, human beings seem to take on the habits of carrion crows and are not satisfied until they have pulled it to pieces.

I know nothing whatever about supernatural events from personal experiences, the only queer things that have happened to me having been in the way of telepathy and in the non-linear aspect of time. It is difficult to think that every description and investigation of *poltergeist* phenomena is either rank char-latanism or credulity, so I prefer to keep an open mind about them meantime and not mock when a man of science, accustomed to analytical experimentation, says he does not like a house and that queer things are going on within it.

A *poltergeist* began to play tricks on the poor folk in Tigh an Quay. Candles blew out when there was no wind, doors slammed and opened, there were sharp raps on the panelling, an occasional window-pane was smashed, steps were heard where no one trod, and in one of the upper rooms it became increasingly difficult to sleep well. I have never heard that a ghost was actually seen, but the people were oppressed in this room by some presence which was not good.

All these sort of things get on the nerves of simple folk, and how much more so in a dark, high building going to ruin, far from any other house, and where the place had a history of violent deeds. It seems reasonable to believe that in their hypersensitive state they imagined and attributed to the *poltergeist* more than should rightly be borne by it. Let that be as it may, queer events continued to occur and the family at Tigh an Quay was feeling the strain of it all.

When your house becomes afflicted with a *poltergeist*, several

courses are open to you : one is to leave it and let someone else
endure it; another is to study it as an interesting phenomenon,
to which scientific treatment the *poltergeist* often objects and
disappears, or you can call in an exorcist, though this appears
to be one of the skilled professions which have almost disappeared
in this machine age.

Our folk in Tigh an Quay were Presbyterians, but when it
came to *poltergeists* they knew something more ancient was
required than plain matter-of-fact Calvinism. They called in
a man of great natural goodness from South Uist, a Catholic
ship's carpenter, who had much experience of laying ghosts.
He inspected the job thoroughly from cellar to slates, just as
a plumber might investigate a rattle in your water pipes, and his
report was most interesting.

"I can lay this ghost all right," he said, "but you would be
better to let it be and endure it, and let it go in its own time.
If I send it out of here, it's a feeling I have that you will be having
worse trouble of another kind."

But the people had had enough of it, years and years of this
pin-pricking worry in a scene of gathering doom. We shall
have to chance that, they said in effect, but please set us free
of this meantime. So the man of great natural goodness from
South Uist exorcized the *poltergeist*, and as far as I have heard—
and know from our own life here—the supernatural joker
played no more tricks in the house. What, pray, was the good
man's recipe—the power to give confidence, or what ? I imagine
he acted honestly.

The family at Tigh an Quay then began to pay the price of
the exorcism. They paid in sickness when they had previously
been so healthy; two members were drowned; cattle died;
the rotten woodwork of the house itself was crumbling.

When we first came here there was a small roofless dry-stone
building to the north of the Planestones, which, from the
structure of the floor, we rightly judged to have been a byre.
Why, we thought, should they make this when there are so
many old buildings ? The answer is a pathetic one—the poor
folk thought that if they built a new byre they might break the
spell which was killing their stock. But doom was gathering
momentum for Tigh an Quay and its occupants; there was

no respite. The last member of the family, who left the place in 1923, was suffering from a nervous breakdown, an extremely uncommon ill in the Highlands.

Doom had fallen. Tigh an Quay lay empty, windows disappearing, slates flying in the gales, the timber mouldering. As we trod about the rotten floors in our early explorations we felt the pathos of this unfortunate family's life here. We could feel so much of it in that usage of the place by them which was still apparent. We read the newspapers which lined the walls below about six layers of lurid wallpaper. There was a *New York Herald* with pen-and-ink illustrations and an account of a notorious gunman of the '80s having been shot in a saloon out West somewhere. There was an English newspaper reporting the Duke of Cambridge's statement in the House of Lords concerning the death of the Prince Imperial in the Zulu War. A bit of a Scottish paper, undated but probably fifty years old, announced that the valuable Burra Islands in Shetland were for sale. And in the haunted room were two coverless and much-thumbed Gaelic Bibles.

We might well wonder what is going to happen to us now that Tigh an Quay is our home. The place had reached a nadir of poverty and lovelessness when we came, a state which did not cause us to shun it, but to offer it love. That we can and do give it in plenty, and such money as we have to spare. But love to Tigh an Quay means the ardent labour of our hands, first given for little in return. Tigh an Quay is hearing happy laughter again, our hands are cleaning its besmirched face, and unless I am greatly wrong our love is driving away its long sleep of doom.

Chapter 5

HOUSEWARMING

WE were still at the Brae House, Dundonnell, on a
Thursday in May, 1938, finishing odds and ends of
correspondence and proof-reading, but feeling certain
we would get away to Tanera by the Saturday if the weather
held good. And then we saw a car pull up at the foot of the
brae and a figure walk up the hill towards the house. I knew
the broad smile visible before I could see the features clearly.
It was George Waterston, the Midlothian bird-watcher. For
sheer energy in the craft and organizing ability among his
fellow-ornithologists there are few to equal George. The valuable migration records which came from the Isle of May before
this second war and the concerted keenness of bird-watchers on
the southern shore of the Firth of Forth were due in no small
measure to his energy. He is the sort of man who is always
bird-watching whatever he is doing. His infective interest is
evident in the tale of his trip to Finnish Lappland. There he
found himself peering over the Russian frontier through his
magnificent pair of binoculars, and the Soviet frontier guards
came across the boundary and took him into their post. Bird-
watching indeed! Anyway, George was their prisoner for a
few days, but in that time he had his captors creeping about
in the birch scrub getting their first exciting lessons in the
art.

"The only thing I was scared of," he said to me, "was if they
should close on to my binoculars."

And now, as I write, George is languishing in a German prison
camp, a victim of the Cretan disaster. He was getting on well
with his study of the birds of Crete until the German invasion
interrupted it, and the latest news is that the Germans have
changed his camp again, just as he was getting upsides with the
ornithology of Oflag —. How deeply we grieve for a prisoner,
but we need not fear for George and any more there may be
like him, because his unflagging interest in a hobby which may

be followed in almost any country of the globe will sustain his
spirit and save him from brooding.

Well, here was George at the Brae. He could stay a night
and come back for the week-end. But we suggested he go
on to Achiltibuie and we would pick him up from there and
take him to Tanera instead. So George went off the following
morning and we continued our packing and sorting and got
our stuff down to the boathouse on the south shore of Little
Loch Broom where the launch was moored. For now we were
no longer dependent on chartering a boat; an access of funds
had enabled us to take advantage of an unusual opportunity
of buying secondhand one of the best launches that have ever
been on this stretch of coast. She has been and still is our faithful
friend and servant; life on Tanera would be difficult without
her, and we could not have done much of what we have in the
way of improving the property without the help of her liberal
design and good timber.

We were going to Tanera, but as Tigh an Quay was roofless
and forlorn, the Brae House still remained the home and head-
quarters. In fact, we kept it for another two years, spending
a few nights there from time to time on our journeys to the
east. This departure on a new and quite different island trip
was a calm and easy affair compared with those journeys in
previous years to Eilean a' Chleirich. We were not going for
a six months' stay with limited contact with the outside world,
but to an island less than two miles from the mainland, with
a good anchorage and having our own boat. It was so easy
that we felt we must be forgetting something. Alasdair was at
school, doubtless wishing he was with us, though we rather
enjoyed this leisurely progress without the ebullient enthusiasm
of childhood.

The sea was flat and calm and the bright sunshine made it
a grand world. Cailleach Head was merely a lump of rock
today by which we could steer closer than ever before instead
of having to stand well out to sea to avoid the choppy water
often found there. The little isles of Carn nan Sgeir were
coming a wonderful spring green on our starboard side and
I thought to myself they would be like a miniature North Rona,
for, unlike the rest of the Summer Isles, Carn nan Sgeir are not

of Torridonian Sandstone but Hebridean Gneiss, the same rock of which Rona is made. Our joy was complete when we came into the Anchorage of Tanera and into the harbour of Tigh an Quay at high tide. The decrepitude of that quay was hidden from our eyes by the tide and this sunshine. We drew alongside, near the head of the quay, and with an ease we had never known on Eilean a' Chleirich or the Treshnish Isles, put our gear ashore, moored the launch and came on land to choose a site for the tent.

You will understand that the grazing of our property was still let to the proprietor of the rest of Tanera and it would be some time before we could take it over ourselves. So in deference to him we felt we could scarcely set up our bell tent in the Little Irish Park by the apple trees, where he would be taking a crop of hay eventually. Instead, we placed it where you see it in the photograph of the ruin, sheltered to some extent from the west and in nobody's way.

We began to learn something of Tanera that very night when the rain came; steady, calm, unending rain, all night long. I woke the following morning to remark there was a pool in the tent, and as I looked about it was obvious I had made an understatement. The tent was in a pool or slowly running stream of water which was not the accumulated rain fallen near the tent but part of that of a very large catchment area which all came down into the deep stone drain which actually ran beneath our tent. I learned then what I have since had plenty of time and opportunity to ponder, that if our glen were ever to be good arable ground I should have to dig a deep open ditch all the way from the sea to the top of the park, with one or two open subsidiary drains leading into it. The whole place is well drained by the old-fashioned stone culverts known as eye drains, so called from the shape of the inside. These work well, but they are not sufficiently large to carry off a spate of water from about two hundred acres of hill.

There was nothing for it but to move round to the good dry ground of the Little Irish Park, in the lee of the apple trees which were then full of blossom. And there the tent remained till we went to Rona early in July. It was a good place altogether: we could hear the willow warblers in the apple

trees before we rose in the morning, and morning and evening
the pied wagtails would hover like little hawks a foot or two
above the grass around us and perch on our tent pegs.

George Waterston came the next day and we explored a
Tanera which was almost as new to me as to him. I remember
our going to the north-west corner of the island overlooking
that lovely little bay called Acairsead Driseach—the anchorage
of the thorn trees. The sun lighted the sea and the northern
half of the Summer Isles, and there below us in the calm water
of the bay all manner of things happened to delight the eyes
of a bird-watcher. A pair of red-throated divers were fishing
there, down from the freshwater loch at the back of us where
they had begun nesting. Eider ducks and drakes were there
in numbers, idling on the blue water and voicing that croon
of theirs which is as the very breath of the northern spring.
Another island sound was the perpetual chittering of Arctic
terns which were newly come to the skerry immediately north
of Eilean na Saille. Common seals were basking on the bare
rock in the middle of the bay, and the sleek heads of others
shone in the sun as they rose from the water of that calm place.
And we saw there that day what I have never seen since around
Tanera, a sheld-duck with a brood of newly hatched young.
I was there in the following year with another bird-watching
friend and saw a pair of velvet scoters, a species which I think
must breed occasionally in the Summer Isles, for not only have
I seen the adult velvet scoters since then, but once when we were
on Eilean a' Chleirich I met a half-fledged duckling on the sea
when I was out fishing in the canoe.

A brisk west wind was blowing on the last day of George's
short visit, and partly to see the cormorants nesting on Carn
Iar, partly to see what the launch would do, we went north
about out of the Anchorage of Tanera, with my neighbour
at the tiller. We reached the open sea off the northern overhung
cliff of Tanera Beag, where for some reason the waves have a
tendency to pile up steep and big. Even on a flat calm day
there is always a heave on the sea just there.

"Shall I ease her off a bit?" I asked my neighbour.

"No, she's all right; keep her to it."

So I just let myself enjoy it. It was my boat, but it was in charge of a man of experience far beyond mine. We found she was a very wet boat, but her action and response were wonderful. Sometimes she seemed to stand upright climbing the top of a wave, and this she did perfectly, with no tendency to split them and go through. The launch was also remarkably free from roll, a characteristic in her for which I have always been thankful in view of my capacity for being seasick.

They were busy weeks which followed—checking observations among the islands, frequently going to Dundonnell on errands connected with the expedition to Rona, and enjoying the mobility given us by the launch. Sometimes in the evenings we would put a few stones in position on the quay and think wistfully of the finished job. Then my friend Leicester Payne came to us for his holiday, and out of the back of his car he produced with a flourish—a crowbar! He lives a life of business and wishes he did not, and now, clear of all the world for a fortnight and primed by my earlier enthusiastic letters, he was going to enjoy himself in his own way. How happy we were together, delving into the ruin and the quay and talking of its possibilities! Leicester is a little man, I am a big one, and a job that I will do by brute strength and with little forethought he will do by science, with careful preparation and with most irritating neatness. Thus we worked together perfectly on that quay, with many a quip at each other for that quality the one of us lacked. We were still young men—for the war had not come then to make us realize we were not the youngest generation of men—but Leicester surprised me one day in the middle of our work when he lapsed into the Yorkshire tongue he knows so well.

"Dost realize, me lad, that this year thee and me 'ave known one another for a quarter of a century?"

And we fell to talking of those early days when we would walk the high edges of millstone grit searching for the caterpillars and cocoons of emperor and oak eggar moths. To this day I thrill anew each time I see an emperor caterpillar, heather green, black-banded and bearing tiny spots of purple or yellow. Our own bit of hill here on Tanera carries enough northern eggar and fox moth caterpillars to have made our mouths water in those days.

He and I together found Charles Darwin when we were
fourteen years old. *The Origin of Species* caused an upheaval
in our young minds that took several years to resolve, but the
immediate result of our discovery of Darwin was that we felt
our feet to be on firm ground. Orientation in this new intellectual freedom was a matter of time. I remember also that
we got a little green-backed book, priced sixpence, which was
a biography of T. H. Huxley by Gerald Leighton. That gave
us another hero and a lot more reading of that lucid expositor's
work. I would not have those striving days back, but they
were great days nevertheless.

Now we were together in those happy days of an island June.
The sun warmed the stones of the quay where we worked, and
I think it was then the quay began to reassume the social quality
such a place acquires in addition to that of mere use. It is a
place where friends can walk and talk or sit and idle if the mood
is right.

The photograph showing the tent and ruin also shows how
a boat could be pulled from the harbour on to the Planestones
across the remains of what had been the terrace shown in
Daniell's print. Back again from there you will notice two
sections of old wall against the gable. The right-hand one
had an ominous lean and needed to be dropped, and much of
the other would also have to come down. Leicester and I
decided to drop those walls and rebuild the terrace, and once
started we found it difficult to stop. Leicester's muscles had
limbered up in the past week to make him fit for anything.
After all, he was here for a holiday and I thought I ought to
get him about in the boat more, and round the islands. We
did make such journeys, most of which were necessary ones
for me, and we had a night out fishing as well, but always
he came back to those walls and that terrace. The long daylight
enabled us to do a day's work after tea, so I gave him his head,
let him boss the job of dropping the walls, and I willingly and
enthusiastically acted as heavy labourer. By the time his last
evening came the terrace was built and filled in with rubble.
It is the world's misfortune as well as ours that Leicester Payne
and I do not work together all our days. He was mentioned
afterwards in this district as "thon little fellow who could work".

VIII. GANNETS OR SOLANS ON THE ROCK FACES OF SULA SGEIR (*see page 91*)

IX*a*. AN ATLANTIC SEAL COW

IX*b*. ATLANTIC GREY SEALS BASKING IN THE SUN

One glorious summer day while Leicester was with us I had the nearest approach to a row it is polite to reach in the West Highlands. I saw a launch early in the morning crossing to the north end of Tanera, then I heard shots, and looking through my binoculars I saw men shooting herring gulls as they flew by the boat. They will be probably going round to the seals in Acairsead Driseach, I thought to myself, and ran across the island to frighten the animals off the skerry, where they would be basking, into the water. They were then pretty safe from these people who like their sport cheap. We had decided to go to Priest Island ourselves that day, and went off northwards, weaving about the islands and skerries as far as Glas Leac Mor. Then we struck across to Glas Leac Beag and noticed the launch of the morning going south from there to the east bay of Eilean a' Chleirich. This island had been proclaimed a sanctuary by Lord Tarbat and it was my unofficial job to see it was kept as one, so we gave chase and reached the island four hundred yards behind the party.

The boatman was still in the launch, a fellow we like well enough, and his comment was one of admiration for our speed. We were soon ashore in our dinghy, and from the noise being made by the peregrine falcons I knew what the objective was— young falcons for visitors at a pound apiece. My speed on the hill is as good as that of most, so I reached the foot of the little cliff as soon as the other fellows. One showed his displeasure quite obviously, but I take my hat off to the other, who came forward with a smile and an open hand:

"Ah! How are you, Doctor? Lovely day, isn't it?"

I was just as charming myself, and we went on to recount to each other a few anecdotes of natural history. There was no touch of rancour.

"The peregrines are making an awful row, aren't they?" I said.

"Yes; terrible noise that. I wouldn't be surprised if they had an eyrie somewhere up in those rocks, if anyone had the time to look for it."

As I had all day to spend on the island and showed no signs of leaving that braeface, I won the round and the falcons got away all right that year. But from what I heard later, the remarks

passed on me were not complimentary. I felt no animosity
to the fellow sent to get the falcons, because it meant a couple
of pounds to him and how should he be expected to let such
a sum pass through his fingers? It is the man behind who is
the trouble, and those of this countryside who encourage visitors
with promises of cheap sport at the expense of the natural fauna.
The peregrine is fairly safe anyway, but the resident race of
grey lag geese is in peril.

We had brought to Tanera a pair of Syrian hamsters which
had been given me by a zoological colleague. These little
rodents are between a mouse and a rat in size, chestnut-coloured
with a white chest and belly and black pencillings about the
face. They have rather blunt noses, large black eyes and very
short tails. Their behaviour is extremely funny to watch as
a travesty of human connubial life. The male is an explorer,
the female a conserver and much inclined to henpeck. You
can give these animals as much food as you like and they will
cram it into their elastic cheek pouches and carry it to some
corner to bury it in the straw. The female will do this much
longer than the male, scurrying between the supply and the
dump, disgorging it from the pouches with the help of the
forepaws pressing from the outside, pulling the straw over and
running back again. Then sometimes she will have him in
her nest and sometimes she won't, and there seems no certainty,
such as impending motherhood, just when she intends to heave
him out. The male is a patient, quiet, long-suffering creature
who makes a nest for himself near the female's, but unlike
birds and men he is a poor builder: she makes an intricate
domed nest, beautiful to see, and his is little more than a hollow
in the straw without any roof.

Leicester had never seen these animals before. He used to
have them out at tea and supper-time and watch them with
a fascinated smile on his face. We were soon going to Rona,
and though I was prepared to take the hamsters there, I was
not keen to impose a further complication on our ménage.
Leicester was delighted when I offered them to him, but on
the morning he was due to leave, and when a rising wind made
us eager to see him safely landed on the mainland, he began
making a travelling cage for them. It was now that the difference

between him and me was sharply prominent: I should have put them in a box with plenty of straw and soaked food and greenstuff for the journey and nailed a bit of rough wood on top, but Leicester *made* a box just the size he wanted to fit in a corner of his well-loaded car; he took out his pocket rule, measured wood on both sides, squared it with his pencil and proceeded to saw it through.

I was getting desperate.

But that was nothing; he went on to chisel the rough-sawn ends, making a nesting compartment and smooth off the whole job.

"Look here," I said, "would you like me to slip across and fetch you some french polish?"

He gave me an expansive smile and continued quite unruffled. The last I saw of him that trip was walking up from the shore as we pulled away in the dinghy, rucksack on his back and hamster cage held carefully before him as if it were the crown jewels.

It was our intention at this time to rent and repair a very small cottage from our neighbour. There was the earth floor to be dug out and made ready for a wooden floor, the walls to be lined with matchboarding and the place partitioned into rooms. We did get more than half the floor out before it was time to leave for Dundonnell and the South to make our final preparations for Rona. Our neighbour put in the floor while we were away on that island, but as nothing else would be done we were not greatly looking forward to the following year when it was likely to be our temporary home.

I have already described in *Island Years* how we were not able to get back to Tanera until the very day in July that we were due to leave for Rona. In fact, the Fishery Cruiser was there in the Anchorage as we came in from Dundonnell in the launch. That day was the last of Tanera we saw for six months. until the cruiser brought us back on 22nd December.

It was intensely cold weather then and the island at its barest, yet it looked almost sub-tropical to us after Rona, where the winter herbage was flush with the soil and blackened by wind and spray and the passage of seals. Here on Tanera were a few little rowan and birch trees and the heather came up round the boot tops. The ruin looked a sorry place then, but it did not depress us : we were going home for Christmas and the wood fires of the Brae House were but a few hours ahead. So farewell to Tanera in 1938.

From the coldness of its Anchorage we went slowly to the noticeably greater coldness of Little Loch Broom, where the Ardessie Falls were frozen solid and the brackish water at the head of the Loch was frozen from shore to shore. The increasing cold got me properly by the short hairs of the neck, for I was sitting on deck with the Chief giving me my first haircut since July.

Chapter 6

1939

THE condition to which I had been reduced by two months in London, Oxford, Cambridge, Glasgow and Edinburgh may be judged when I record that in attending a dinner of the Scottish Ornithological Club in Edinburgh in March I declined the soup, played with the fish, skipped the roast beef, asked for a very small helping of the trifle, and finished with a biscuit and butter and the coffee. Three months before, on Rona, the very thought of roast beef and greens had been at once a joy and a pain of anticipation. Everybody in the South had done us too well, and because we like our food and had enjoyed meeting our friends, both Bobbie and I had overlooked the fact that such normally active people as ourselves ought to do morning exercises or subscribe to a gymnasium when we were away from the fat-consuming air of the North-West. Bobbie had had three colds and influenza during the time we were in London, for the resistance of the remote islander to the common ills of urban life is very low. I had fared better and attribute my freedom to the fact that during the whole time I never entered train, tram or 'bus, but used my old open Ford car to get me about in London. Incidentally, I learned my way about that great city and found it by far the easiest town of any we visited in which to drive a car. The traffic in London has more freedom than elsewhere and appears to interpret regulations with more common sense. Only once did I make a foolish mistake in the lines at a wide Y junction when I was about to take the right-hand arm, and the reproach from an oncoming London 'bus driver still makes my ears tingle :

"I suppose you'd like me to get down out of me cab," he said, pointing across the wide expanse to my left, "and pull those railings up so that even you could get by !"

This job of being my own taxi-man cost me rather a lot of money parking the car, though I found one open car park somewhere behind Victoria Station where you could leave it all day

for a shilling, and there was a most cheerful old man in charge.
I remember coming along about eleven o'clock on the night
of New Year's Day when wind and rain were still making
London as unpleasant as when I had come up in the morning.
The old man and I exchanged greetings and compliments of
the season, and then he swore at the weather. I told him it
often rained like this where I came from, but that our rain was
clean and the wind soon blew us dry.

"And where would that be?" he asked.

I tried to explain some British geography, of which the
Londoner of all men is so complacently ignorant. He was
aghast at the idea of a railway being sixty miles away and the
nearest market town seventy-five miles.

"Coo! If you'll excuse me saying so, sir, you're what I
should call a bit of a savage!"

Well, here we were at Dundonnell at last, finishing more
odds and ends before returning again to our savage life. The
launch had been laid up all winter on Tanera, so we had to
gather all we were going to take in the car and go round by
road to Badentarbet Pier. It was late on an early May evening
when all our gear was ashore below the little cottage on the
hillside. The floor was in—almost—but no partitions and no
lining, so we had in effect one long room with an open fireplace
at each end. The door had rotted away at the foot sufficient
to allow a dog room to get in and out, but we were able to
prop sacks against the hole and realized the luxury of having
rigid walls and a good roof about us.

Potatoes should have been in the ground before this time, and
here were we with not a spit of earth dug. I began work on
the following morning at the east side of the Little Irish Park,
where a large bed of dockens and nettles were now pushing
ahead for the summer's growth. Nettles do not grow on bad
ground, neither do dockens of the strength these were, but to
get an old nettle-bed to look like a garden means a spell of
tribulation, to which I, soft and flabby from the winter months
of luxurious living, came with full knowledge and some shyness.
I dug a trench 18 inches wide and 15 inches deep, then pared
off the nettles and dockens of the next one and deposited them
upside down in the bottom. Bobbie cut and carried seaweed

which was put on the upturned nettles, and finally the bared soil of the second trench to be was loosened with a pickaxe and then dug over the seaweed in the first trench.

This technique was followed throughout till we had enough ground for potatoes, cabbage and kale. How I suffered! The winter's fat fell away from me, and after a week of hardly knowing how to get on my feet once I was down on my back, I began to limber up and enjoy the work. Blisters burst and hardened into "hooves" which have not left my hands since. Furthermore, the soil there was very deep and of beautiful quality and it stimulated me to see the patch of fresh brown earth growing larger each day. The growth of everything we planted there was enormous, and even now in 1942 there is no better bit of the garden than Nettlebed Piece.

Those three or four weeks Bobbie and I lived on the floor of that cottage, becoming so gloriously tired with the gardening, have made a very happy memory. Our meals were simple, but among them there stood out a daily dish we had never been able to have before in our island years—nettle purée—for nettles grow only where man has lived and tilled for a long time. Let me tell you exactly how we make this really delicious but generally despised dish: pick a large quantity of *young* nettles, and put the top four leaves only of each stalk into a saucepan. Press them down well, add a very little water and cook for seven minutes, keeping the nettles moving and pounding them gently with a wooden spirtle; do not strain, add a lump of butter and pepper and salt, and eat immediately. Nettle apologists often say they are quite as good as spinach, but I should never apologize for nettles, because they are a delicacy far in advance of spinach, with a fine flavour all their own. I knew of one old Highland gentleman who said he felt no man at all for the rest of the year if he did not get at least three boilings of nettles in the spring. We also had plenty of winkles from our own beach and found they were an excellent meal in conjunction with the nettles. The winkles were put in cold water and boiled for one minute.

I also painted the launch before putting her on the water, and in this practical sense I wondered anew at the remarkable drying power of the Highland May and June when the sun

often shines its full span of about sixteen hours a day and the
prevalent northerly breeze desiccates everything which does
not have its roots well in the ground. This is the time when
boat seams open and the paint almost dries under the brush
as it is applied. The north wind of May and June can be cold
if you are standing about on a job, yet as soon as you step out
of the wind and still remain in the sun the air is baking hot.
The afternoons are best spent lazing about if the time can be
spared, though on Tanera we have had to cut down the time
of our usual island siestas. We do try to have a rest each summer
day after lunch, because the daylight is so long and the evening
such a delightful time in which to work that we often have to
compel ourselves to come indoors at midnight.

Cuddy fishing is another hindrance to regular hours in May,
when these young coalfish are in the vicinity of isolated skerries
and will take a coarse white fly trailed below the surface on a
bamboo rod. We go about ten o'clock on a dead calm evening
and wait for the cuddies to rise. They leap in thousands from
the water to make the surface for many yards around dance
and sound as if heavy tropical rain were falling. A basketful
of fish takes little getting on such a night and we come home
in the half-light with plenty of song, gutting and cleaning the
fish as we go. Some to eat, some to salt and some to give away
to friends on the overside. The guts we keep in a bucket to
put on the compost heap; such excellent, readily decaying
organic matter is not to be wasted.

It was in May that we managed to rent the schoolhouse of
Tanera, an ugly, meagrely built place set high on a cliff looking
south-east over the Anchorage. We were glad to get it, for
we could now bring our furniture from Dundonnell and set
up house more conveniently than in the cottage. The large,
draughty schoolroom would do as a dining-room in summer
when we should have lots of friends coming. We painted
and papered and scrubbed, though we never managed to make
the place look really nice. The woodwork was too poor for
that, and there was an atmosphere about the house which we
did not like very much. There is no garden or fence round
the place, just a very poor black moor, scarred by turf cutting:
the great thing to be said for that house is its view, which is a

superb panorama of sea, wild coast and the mountains of
Sutherland and Ross. The house has lain unused as a school
since before the 1914 war, the registers of that period still lying
in an outbuilding at the back. What we cannot understand is
why the school should be set up there, far from most of the
other houses and entailing a journey for the children from one
half of the island along a cliff edge where the path is continually
crumbling and dangerous for man or beast. The house was
built about 1870, I believe, and the story goes that the women
of the island carried up the stone and lime for the job, their
husbands being away for the fishing. Having now carried
several tons of stuff up and down there on my own back, I can
salute those women and wonder the more at the odd choice
of site.

I had been to a funeral on the mainland one day in May,
and was sitting with Donnie Fraser in his mother's house when
a young man walked in whom I did not know. He was fair,
bright blue of eye, lean as a falcon, with a well-poised head, and
dressed in blue jersey, breeches and heavy boots. I liked the
make of him and was able to take such full stock because I was
sitting in a dark corner. I was a little surprised when he asked
for me, though I had guessed from those boots that he was
a climber and therefore no native of these parts. It was Alastair
Cram, one of the score best climbers in Britain, with every one
of the five hundred and forty-three Munroes or 3000-foot hills
in Scotland to his credit, and more than anything else, we knew
him to be a friend of Kenneth Dougal MacDougall, our own
Dougal of the island years. When he walked into Donnie
Fraser's he had been living in the hill for a month or more.

What an extraordinarily open and innocent face for a lawyer,
I had thought to myself immediately, but soon I saw how his
face could be that of the mystic and idealist he is in one moment,
and of the sharp, practical man of affairs the next. The dualism
was in his character as well as in his face, and the warring of
these two sides had brought him here now, the mystic in the
ascendant. He came across with us to stay for two or three
days, and it seemed as if he were glad to sever by a mile or
two of sea his few remaining bonds with the lawyer's life.
Tanera became a stage in his journey, for he remained with

us three months and would have gone to Rona with us for the winter had not the war fallen upon all our plans. He left for Switzerland in August and got back only just in time.

And now, as I write this, word has reached us that Alastair Cram, the seeker of experience, has fallen a prisoner in the second Libyan campaign and is now in Italy, with the high Alps in his view from the prison camp. His reaction to prison life will be different from that of George Waterston, but I think he will gather strength from the experience nevertheless. Professor Toynbee in his *A Study of History* discusses at length the concept of Withdrawal and Return as a potent influence in the spiritual development of individuals. He shows how a period of withdrawal from the world may strengthen a man so that when he returns he gives forth of an energy he did not know he possessed. Christ began His mission after His forty days in the wilderness; St. Ignatius de Loyola became the founder of his Order after the withdrawal caused by his severe wounds at Pampeluna. It all depends on the attitude of mind in which withdrawal is faced. The truth of the concept is dimly realized by many of us as young men. It was at the back of my own island years, it has taken expeditions of undergraduates to the Antarctic, Greenland and Labrador. A fault of our civilization is that it denies the wilderness to the great majority of young men.

We had a queer month or two in that brilliant early summer of 1939, which has become a time difficult to remember clearly and assess as part of our life. There was an immense amount of work to be done, but it was all disjointed, and a multitude of figures flitted across our stage before Bobbie and I had really got the feeling of Tanera as home.

Alastair Cram was a godsend to us: he could live on our level and not count it uncomfortable; he could handle a boat, use his hands in many ways, and showed a willingness to learn such skills as he did not command. Bobbie was painting and papering one day at the schoolhouse when he looked in and offered quite a lot of useful advice. Bobbie is a careful and good worker but with no pretension to professional skill, so without the least touch of irony—for it is not in her—she suggested he should take over. This he did while Bobbie and I went off to

another job. We did not return till tea-time, when we found
Alastair Cram sitting on his heels in the middle of the room,
his paint-soiled hands hanging over his knees and the mop
of fair curly hair showing unmistakable signs of terra-cotta paint.
There was also more paint about the room than there should
be. Bobbie was respectfully quiet, but I immediately thought
of that bouncy one in A. A. Milne's *Winnie-the-Pooh* books.
Restraint of comment has never been one of my virtues.

"Tiggers don't paint houses," I said.

"Frank!" said Bobbie, at once shocked and remonstrating
with me, but I was not bothered, for Alastair Cram was now on
his back laughing uproariously, acclaiming my aptness.

We had also to cut peats during that good weather, and
I started a bank near the house where there appeared to be
about four feet of peat. It was black, stinking stuff I found
when I got into it, that black, fibreless peat which is highly
charged with sulphuretted hydrogen and which crumbles easily
under the turf spade. Pieces of bogwood were also interspersed
through it, making it difficult for me to keep a clean, straight
face of peat. Alastair Cram had carefully observed the beautiful
peat-faces in the bog which is cut by the Coigach crofters
and he was not greatly pleased with mine. I could see he was
itching to do it himself, so I turned over the job to him and
when Bobbie came along to help I left them to it, not returning
till much later in the afternoon. I looked at the pock-marked
peat-hag which had been at least straight earlier in the day
and regular in its spade-marks. Alastair Cram looked at me
and at the job, and he knew what was coming. From that
moment his name was Tigger or, in our own diminutive,
Tigsie.

Bobbie asked me to come and help, but I would not, and
made some excuse for doing something else.

Next day Tigsie and I were walking down to Tigh an Quay
and as we passed the peat-face he said:

"Look here, Frank, why didn't you take the spade out of my
hands yesterday and tell me to get to hell out of it? I deserved it."

"For this reason," I said: "you came here of your own free
will; you took up the tool to do a job for us, with intent to
help. You found you couldn't do it as well in practice as your

observation of peat cutting had led you to believe. The more expert a craftsman is, the easier does his work appear to the onlooker, and you had been watching crofters born to it cutting peat of quite different quality from this. Had you been a paid labourer I should have given you a good blowing up, but you were not; you were a free man trying to help and trying to learn, and it was not for me to be cross and prevent you learning and experimenting. Now you know there are different kinds of peat; you know it doesn't really pay to dip into the face horizontally; and you will have a greater respect for those chaps over yonder when you see them slicing away and turning out nice cheesy peats."

Tigsie accepted this outlook and tried many a skill in the following months his hands had never known before. But of some things he was complete master, and I found it interesting to watch the difference the sureness of mastery made to him. The engine of the launch was an example : I am a very poor hand with engines and am inclined to neglect them, partly because I do not know enough about them and partly because they do not interest me as long as they do their work. Tigsie was not satisfied with our engine, and it says much for my confidence in him when I let him take it down and reassemble it. One of my most enduring memories of him is that of the sunlight of June, the launch in the harbour leaning on fenders against the quay, and amidships a fair head of hair just visible above the gunwale. Hour after hour he stayed there, silent except for the occasional sound of a tool, and with immense concentration. Then one day he climbed out of the boat, quite casually, and said, "I think you'll find her run a bit better now."

So she did; decarbonized, valves ground, tappets adjusted, all rust from the outside of the engine sandpapered off and the whole repainted, it has needed no attention in the three years since then.

Moving furniture from the Brae House to Tanera was no light job, though the help Tigsie and Donnie Fraser gave us made it possible to do it ourselves. Bobbie and I went round to Dundonnell in the Ford for a night or two at a time and carried stuff in the car to the boathouse. Donnie and Tigsie brought the launch from Tanera if the weather was fit; we stowed the cargo together and drank a quart of tea, and then we would return to Tanera our respective ways and join forces for the back-breaking work of getting everything from the shore up to the schoolhouse.

Leicester Payne came for his second Tanera holiday at this time and joined the launch party. They met a bit of sea one day off Cailleach Head when returning with a load, and to make things worse the engine stopped time after time. The trouble was rust from the inside of the petrol tank getting into the carburettor and blocking the flow of petrol. Donnie Fraser and Tigsie were busy with the seamanship, and the peculiar gifts of Leicester Payne now came into play. That exasperating slowness, thoroughness and obliviousness of surrounding circumstances were just the qualities required. Leicester removed the tank and petrol pipe, emptied them and washed them out and put back clean petrol; he took down the carburettor and reassembled it, all with the surest of hands despite the violent motion of the boat. Here were three men on top of their job, and I wondered to myself afterwards, when I heard of the episode, how far I had been to blame for the condition of that petrol tank, which had now begun to leak in several places. Anyway, I learned a lesson, bought a new petrol tank, and have since then sieved the petrol carefully through two thicknesses of calico. But drops of water and fragments of rust still seem to get in, so we now make it routine to wash the tank out every three months.

Leicester's interest in rebuilding the quay was just as keen this year as last, and in face of the many distractions such as the furniture removal we did get a few days' work at it. We pulled down the dry-stone walls of that pathetic little byre on the Planestones which the old folk had built in the hope of eluding the evil spell on the place. It was good to see it gone, and the stone was used in rebuilding the sea wall or parapet along the front of the Planestones at right angles to the quay, on which the man is sitting in Daniell's print.

Those were the best days of his holiday, because a short summer visit to Rona was impending, but uncertain as to actual date. Rightly we should have gone in May, but the cruiser had had to go in dock for engine trouble. She came in now on Sunday morning, 18th June, as Leicester and I were planting kale, so it was bundle and go for Bobbie and me. The last I saw of Leicester was in the dinghy below me as I leaned over the rail of the ship; it was an effort not to reach down and lift the little man inboard by the scruff of his neck and whisk him away to the remoteness of Rona. Had I done so I know he would not have cared a damn, for he would have lived for once in the moment and faced the uproar in his business and family circles when the time came.

And yet, of course, he would have cared, and so should I, not for the immediate consequences of a rash decision, but because it would have been escapism, running away from what he did not like. That way is despicable. I get a fairly large mail from people who want to live an island life and who ask me how they should set about it. First of all, their approach is wrong—you have to discover entirely for yourself how you are going to live such a life; and secondly, their outlook is usually wrong, because the island life in prospect is escapism pure and simple. You will never be happy on an island if it is something to which you have run away. Come to an island when you have conquered in the life you are already living, and come not as a lotos-eater but with heart and hands ready to meet a challenge. Perhaps I did not see all this as clearly as I do now when I used to yearn for an island, but this ripening of the experience should be passed on—come to an island with a definite job of work in your head and the determination to carry it through. Why did Tigsie come for three days and stay three months? Because he found direction in things and constant hard work.

That same morning the cruiser came for us a 33-foot green schooner, *Southseaman*, had sailed into the Cabbage Patch and dropped anchor. Her owner, Ivan Hulburd, was alone and apparently in no hurry. He came round to Tigh an Quay as we were packing up and introduced himself, and when I apologized for my imminent departure he was quite untroubled, saying he was prepared to lie here a good while. And I saw no more of that jaunty figure in blue jersey, corduroy shorts and plimsolls until we came back from Rona. Tigsie and Leicester saw a

good deal of him in the next few days, so that when Bobbie
and I returned it was as if to meet a friend already made. Ivan
became part and parcel of that extraordinary summer of 1939.
His great laugh must still be echoing about that schoolroom,
and our laughter also, for his humour was inexhaustible and
not unlike that endeared to us through the interpretation of
Mr. Ralph Lynn. Such an exterior in the upper-class Englishman, which makes him appear "a typical English bloody fool",
is a defensive armament which always seems to fool foreigners,
and Scots often enough. It is part of an Englishman's clothes
to appear to be perpetually doing nothing. We found Ivan's
flair to be the training and handling of boys, and as time passed
and Ivan seemed prepared to stay in the Anchorage through
the winter, I had hopes he might have started a troop of Sea
Scouts in Coigach. His knowledge and study of music also
promised well for the social side of our island life, but, like
most growing activities of that fateful year, it was stifled by the
outbreak of war. *Southseaman* is laid up in Oban, and Ivan
has passed through the ranks to become a Captain in the Queen's
Own Royal West Kents.

The kind of incident which delights me and makes me feel
our open house on Tanera is well worth while is exemplified
in Ivan meeting our friends Alec and Beryl Valentine. Ivan
and Alec found they were of the same College at Oxford though
fifteen years apart, and the friendship begun on Tanera has
since developed. And another day we had a visit from two
masters and three boys from Stowe when Margaret Leigh was
staying with us. Each found they had close friends in common
in Oxford, and Ivan added to the general good-fellowship by
giving his delightful burlesque of a *quondam* conductor of the
Bach Choir.

Chapter 7

RONA REVISITED

HERE we are, making for Rona over a sea which was flat
calm so that even I could walk about on deck and accept
an invitation to the bridge. The ship passed a basking
shark half-way across the Minch and put about to ram it. I was
curiously untroubled about the shark, for I felt it was going to
escape, and it did. These great fish heedlessly meandering
through the surface layer of the ocean undoubtedly do much
damage to herring-nets, and it is one of the services the fishery
cruisers do for the fishermen to ram the sharks whenever possible.
As conditions are, this has to be done, but the practice is a
confession of failure on the part of the country to conserve its
wild-life resources. Every one of these fish rammed means
five tons of highly vitaminized oil utterly wasted as well as the
great quantities of meat. The cruiser had killed fifty-three
that season and lots of other ships and drifters had been doing
similar work. How can we complacently accept such waste?
Rightly organized, the capture and utilization of these fish
could provide a small seasonal industry in the West Highlands.
It is an activity which should be in the administrative care of a
Bureau of Biological Survey which some of us were trying
to get established before the war. But it was of little use talking
and beseeching. The pre-war Government of old men was
supine, saying, as it were, "Just leave us alone, please; all we
ask is that you should leave us alone and in peace." In other
words, "Shoo! fly, don't bother me!"

I take the same attitude about the Atlantic grey seals themselves. Were we to conserve them and colonize new island
groups with them, they too would link up with the same local
industry I have suggested for the basking sharks. By the means
I have outlined in *Island Years* we could increase the numbers
of seals and prevent a large proportion of accidental mortality
at the nursery grounds. At this unfortunate moment of our
history, the spring of 1942, we should have been glad of the

80

X*a*. THE PETREL CAME OUT OF
THE NIGHT TOWARDS THE
LENS (*see page* 87)

X*b*. AN EIDER DUCK ON HER
NEST

XI. LEAVING NORTH RONA, JUNE 1939 (*see page 88*)
lowering gear from the cliff to the boat fifty feet below

oil and fats available had this policy of conservation through wise use been in operation. We have much to learn from Russia in this direction : the Soviets have every intention that their wild-life resources shall contribute to the economy of the State, but they are equally intent that their toll shall not be wasteful, uncontrolled exploitation of wild life and they are doing the preliminary ecological research beforehand—not afterwards when numbers have dwindled and species are in danger of extinction. Here in Britain we seem unable to steer a wise course between heedless exploitation and waste on the one hand and sentimental total preservation on the other.

The voyage to Rona was happily uneventful and I came on deck just after six in the morning with the ship slowing down ready to anchor under the magnificent bird cliffs of the Tor of Rona. Oh, the magnificence of the scene ! I must not repeat what I have written already of my first view of Rona, but my emotions were the same again and just as fresh. Now there was the added interest of our two little huts in the sheep fank : were they whole ? The sun was behind us and we could see the shapes of the huts clearly on the low neck of land between the hilly part of Rona and the northern peninsula of Fianuis. They looked all right from the ship, and within a quarter of an hour we were running down from the huts to Geodha Stoth again to tell the waiting launch that they were indeed all right and as we left them six months ago.

How different was this day of high June from that rosy dawn of late December when the snow had quietened Rona ! The seal grounds which were then churned to a deep black mud were now green again, and nothing but the almost indestructible ear bones remained of the hundred and fifty carcasses of seal calves which had lain rotting about the grounds when we left. The great black-backed gulls had done their work well as the island's scavengers. The colony of these birds, 700 or 1000 pairs, was now in full activity of feeding the young ones, and the noise they made resenting our advent was the one unpleasant sound among the hundreds of thousands of bird voices raised about us.

We made an immense breakfast and felt eager to go all over the island as soon as possible. How many seals would there be about the shores, should we find the turnstones nesting

F

as we hoped, and how had our restorations to the chapel of
St. Ronan fared? Bobbie's first act was to go over the large
quantity of stores we had had to leave on the island when
we came away in December, and she was thinking to herself
that although we should need them for the second autumn
expedition to Rona, it would be wise to take them all back
with us to Tanera, because the portents were for war in the
autumn, and if that happened there would be something particularly irritating in thinking of good food lying only eighty-five
miles away but utterly inaccessible to us.

Several years of remote island life have caused me to try
to analyse the emotions which so deeply affect us in the march
of the island seasons. What is the cause of this elevation we
feel in high June, over and above the joy the mainland itself
is giving at that time? First, I think the quality of light raises
our perceptions, heightening as it does the brilliant colours
of the season. The sky is cloudless on these ecstatic days and
therefore limitless. The sea is deep blue, unbroken and also
limitless until the island shores are reached and a band of brilliantly
white surf makes endless patterns of beauty as it falls from the
rocks and rides back to meet the next oncoming swell. A
seal's head rising in this their favourite playground gleams
bright, and as the animal turns and rolls, its belly flashes smooth
and as one with the wave it breaks. The saffron lichen of the
cliffs above the tide and fed by the spray is a vivid reflection
of the sunlight, never clashing with the range of colours displayed
by the cushions of sea-pink which grow as soon as a few grains
of soil can lodge. Never have I seen such a carpet of sea-pink
as on the west side of Rona above Geodha Blatha Mor—there
is little else but sea-pink there and the flowers white, cream,
and every shade between pale pink, rose and a deep red colour
which is almost purple. Then there is the seething, toiling
bird life in an ecstasy of abandon which is not purposeless but
surely functional in the urgency of reproduction. Here is a
vast concourse living in a state of joy, acting in preparation
for hundreds of thousands of new lives. Man, whose aesthetic
reactions have much in common with those of birds, cannot
remain unaffected in the midst of this short summer glory of
light, colour and activity.

The mainland spring and summer rise and unfold gently from the dark cape of winter; summer itself has a length and an evenness the little islands never know, and autumn, which is one of the year's glories where there are trees and shelter, does not come into the island's seasons. The illusion of summer may persist into October, when one gale from the south-east will shrivel the grass and each leaf and flower, and from then till the advent of a laggard spring it is winter.

Late summer and early winter on Rona are made lively by the breeding seals and migrating birds, but the depth of winter is a time of deadness and sleep. Seals are gone, birds are gone, the ground is black and the rock has lost its brightness. And here on Tanera it is much the same; winter offers little in the way of wild life except the pageant of the wild geese, and it comes suddenly. So much of an island's bird life is seasonal, and its mammalian population is usually limited and in poor variety. If there is natural shelter on an island or a walled garden, then a little place becomes an oasis where leaves fall gracefully or may persist through the winter. Small birds flock to it and the human heart is cheered.

The mainland winter in a sheltered glen is no dead time. Indeed, the observer may see more living things then, for the leafless trees do not hide the birds and new-fallen snow is a new edition of a very old book of natural history wherein is described in meticulous detail the habits and movements of bird and beast. Busy flocks of mixed tits go from tree to tree, the deer come close about the house, and robins and chaffinches come indoors.

Quietness and the colourings of sea and sky make the beauty of an island winter, though storms can make those moments rare. Storms may be beautiful, but a continuance of them is not felt to be so by the island dweller whose nights are made wretched and whose thoughts are constantly running over the possibility of damage to boats, stacks of hay or corn and roofs of buildings. The cruel inexorable quality of a south-easterly gale lasting from ten days to three weeks deadens perception of beauty and leaves the nerves raw.

But the rapid crescendo through spring to the ecstasy of high June repays the islander, and there he stays. Even then he and his avian companions are not free from the threat of devastation, for a northerly gale is not uncommon in late June. I described in *Island Years* the effects of such a gale on the gulleries of Eilean a' Chleirich in 1937 when hard-driven rain and breaking seas killed many young birds. And now on Rona the same thing happened in 1939. We made our quick run round the island on that first day in warmth and sunshine, enjoying every moment and delighting in each place seen again and anew. Then it began to blow cold under heavily clouded skies. We were wearing as much as we did in December, glad of every stitch of it and especially of our Grenfell suits. Birds cowered near their nests, guillemots bunched together on their ledges and faced the cliff, and many of the lower kittiwakes' nests were blown or washed away altogether.

A trawler called *City of Leeds* anchored under the south side of Rona, but the immense swell in this northern ocean gave her no quiet berth. She rolled at incredible angles and I thanked my lucky stars I was not aboard her. How did they manage to keep water in a kettle or tea in a cup ? The skipper seemed to spend a lot of his time during those three days in his raised wheelhouse. I could not see his look of surprise at seeing me on Rona, but it was obvious enough in his gestures as he shot head and shoulders out of the window and gave me a wave.

And imagine my surprise when I saw another visitor from civilization taking shelter on the south side of Rona ! It was a cock homing pigeon complete with identification- and race-rings. Where on earth had he come from ? He was tired but had not quite enough confidence to come to my hand. I was sorry, for I could have fed him—though not on maple peas—and my heart warmed to this little brother of the gale. How much I would have liked to know his origin ! Perhaps he came from the real City of Leeds or Barnsley or somewhere in that great pet-loving tract of industrial England. I imagined his owner as a man with a walrus moustache and a bowler hat set on the back of his head, looking from time to time into his pigeon trap, little knowing his bird was sheltering on Britain's loneliest island. Or again he may have been a Royal Air Force pigeon from an Orkney station.

There is immense pleasure in wandering over well-known or

well-loved ground which has been lost for a spell. We knew this Rona of summer, yet the fact that we were here last in midwinter made the scene one of new interest and contrast. I went down to Sceapull, the south-west corner of Rona, thinking of six months ago when that place was almost disappearing under the great seas which broke over Loba Sgeir and Harsgeir. An old bull seal had died on top of the promontory and I wondered if his skull would be clear now. But it takes more than one winter to disintegrate such a beast in this climate— the gulls had not yet managed to pull his thick hide to shreds. I was surprised to see some coarse twine lying near the carcass and, as an islander does with any strange thing in his little kingdom, I examined it closely and asked how it could have got there. It was not twine at all but the intestines of the seal. The gulls had pulled them out of his belly in the winter, twisted and twisted them in an effort to pull them to pieces, and given up the job when they found it too much for them. In this extended state the sun had dried those great guts into a rope of uncommon strength. I measured fourteen yards of them, and after stretching with all my weight they came to eighteen yards of light thong, beautifully cured by natural means. Was it from such accidents as this that primitive man first found the way to use the intestines of carnivorous animals for strings? If violin strings are catgut, my seal rope would make a G string for the bass viol of Fionn MacCoull!

We found fulmars nesting under the same rocks where they were last year, a pair of razorbills on the same precarious tuft of sea-pink on the sheer surface of the red column of the western cliff of Rona, and at night we heard a storm petrel with a peculiar voice in the same place in the dyke round the huts as it was last year. We had been far since last we had heard her funny voice making a noise like "recherche", but it was fairly certain she had been farther.

Our restorations to Ronan's chapel and cell were intact. I looked at the stone which was the last one I handled in the work in December: it was long and flat, laid to provide a gangplank for the fulmar petrels from the lower level of the cell and altar stones to the later level of the chapel floor. I had squashed the end of the middle finger of my left hand in letting it down into place, and now as I looked in June a new nail to my finger had almost replaced the blackened one and a fulmar petrel was nesting each side of the altar in the dark cell.

Bobbie and I went to the chapel ruins at midnight on the second day of our return, to experience again the wonderful aerial dance of the Leach's fork-tailed petrels; but we were disappointed, for the northerly gale had lessened their activity to little or nothing. I was still anxious to get a flash-bulb photograph of one of the petrels in flight and came prepared to waste a dozen bulbs to get this unique picture. As I have said, the wind blew for nearly a week so I wasted no more sleep until it dropped, except on the night of my birthday, which is Midsummer's Eve. This was my thirty-sixth, and my fourth island birthday. Where better could I be than on Rona?

It is my habit to spend the night of my birthday outside, enjoying the wild living things of the particular place where I happen to be. The fork-tailed petrels of North Rona go into my birthday memories now along with the storm petrels of the Clerach, the roe deer and redstarts of the Dundonnell woods, the owls, hedgehogs and warblers of English woodlands and the whaups of Border moors. The activity on this first calm night was remarkable. Hundreds of the birds were flying hither and thither and calling that weird cry which so few people will ever hear. We are apt to think the flight of the birds erratic, because they come and go so quickly, and collide with your face and with each other as they fly. But if you see a petrel fly over one place in the darkness and thereafter watch that place intently, you will find a bird passing over it again in half a minute or so and it will take the same path as it flies on again into the night. It would seem that each bird has a track of flight, up and down and in and out, and follows it fairly accurately, but as the hundreds of other birds also have tracks through the same air over the chapel ruins and timing cannot be exact, the collisions occur and the observer is apt to think the birds' flight more erratic than it really is.

Anyway, I let the observation guide my actions, for having seen a bird come towards me twice over a certain heap of stones and sea-pink, I put the camera to my eye, pointed at the place where the bird should appear. You will understand I could not see through the viewfinder in the dark, but as the firing position of the camera is at the eye, I felt I was more likely to get the bird in from this accustomed position than from any other. Sure enough the bird came, and I let go. The bird came back two or three times more, and each time a flash-bulb lit up the ruins. Activity was waning by two o'clock and we made our way home to the huts, sleepy but well satisfied and wondering what was recorded on that little strip of celluloid.

The result was beyond my expectations—one negative showing the petrel coming out of the night towards the lens. The bird's wings were low in flight, in a characteristic position, well bent at the first joint and showing the great length of wing. For the better reproduction of this picture I have had the lines of the wings touched with an air brush, but nothing has been put in that does not appear in the photograph. The flash-bulb has shown the face white, though it is really grey, and the rest of the plumage is black or dark grey beneath the wings.

It had been my intention to make as good a collection as possible of Rona's insect life and I had come armed with a mass of collecting gear provided by the Royal Scottish Museum. This continual northerly gale and strong wind effectively sent the insects to earth, though I did get some flies by dragging the net over the acres of chickweed on Fianuis, and some beetles by looking under stones.

Observations on the seals turned out more or less as I had expected: that about ten per cent. of the population present in October remained about the island throughout the year, and of that ten per cent. a larger than normal proportion was of yearling seals. There is a definite migration of the seals to and from the breeding ground, but it is not absolute or inelastic. The tendency is for the young seals to remain in the vicinity of the nursery during their first summer, but it is no more than a tendency, for yearling Atlantic grey seals are the worst offenders of the species in robbing salmon-nets along outlying parts of the west and north coasts. These yearlings seem to follow a different migration from the breeding stock, in that those staying about the nursery until August then tend to move away. When we were on the grey seal nursery of the Treshnish Isles in 1937 we rarely saw a yearling seal. It remains an interesting question in animal sociology what governs the behaviour of a small proportion of a predominantly migrant species remaining about the breeding ground throughout the year. The Atlantic grey seal is an interesting animal which is not hidebound in its habits at all. There is this undoubted migratory tendency, though the movements may be short ones of only a few miles, and the habit is not universal. Terrain evidently governs their movement to a large extent. The colony of grey seals on the Farne Islands off the Northumberland coast do not appear to migrate, though individuals leave the herd to visit the estuaries where the salmon are running. The grey seal is mainly a consumer of coarse white fish lying near outlying rocky shores, but a few, especially the yearling seals, break the habit of aloofness and come inshore for the salmon.

The northerly gales abated in just over a week and left a tremendous swell on the sea which broke on the coasts of Rona in showers of spray and with cannonades of sound. But we were now preparing for a few calm midsummer days and the state of the sea was not bothering us very much. Our complacency was shattered when we saw the cruiser come in to the eastern bight of Rona and bob on those immense swells as if she were a dinghy or a fallen leaf.

"We can't go," said Bobbie, "because we shall never be able to get the stores away."

"I'm afraid that story won't do, if the ship has made the journey specially for us, but she's confoundedly early."

I could see through my glass how difficult it was to get the boat lowered, and when eventually the ship's launch came in to Geodha Stoth it was obvious we should have to pick our moment and jump for it—and leave everything—if we were to go from Geodha Stoth.

But Bobbie was not prepared to leave those stores. She went over to Sgeildige Geo and noticed there was an unbroken stretch against the sheer cliff of the south side near the Tunnel Cave. Sure enough it was much more feasible to lower our stuff fifty feet on a rope into a boat in quiet water than to be waiting for chancy moments where the swell was bad at the usual landing. So we signalled the ship to round the north end of the island and come into the western bight.

Bobbie and I packed and roped and carried box after box to the edge of the cliff until the launch came beneath us. It was careful work lowering them all, for had one come loose in mid air it would have done a lot of damage to launch and men beneath. All we left in the huts was a roll of roofing felt and a bag of cement, things which might be useful for the future, whoever should occupy those huts. We have since learnt that the larger hut has blown down, but that the smaller one is sound and has been of service to some unfortunates in this war. That is how it should be.

We ourselves could not go down the ropes, but climbed down the cliffs a little distance away where nine months ago I had tried to pull a newly born calf out of the sea. We jumped for it without mishap and joined the cruiser, which rolled on a sea which was oily calm except for the great swell. There was more difficulty getting the launch inboard again and I could not help thinking what a dangerous business it was. All officers and men concerned realized the danger, and their neat movements, sidesteps and ducks at the right moments, were good to watch; sheets held taut one moment suddenly slackened and the launch would swing across the deck from gunwale to gunwale as she hung from her derrick. Fenders were dropped quickly into position where next moment the boat would strike, and a man would crouch low till the next swing.

This was the first time I had viewed Rona from the western sea and I took my fill of its magnificent coastline while I was still on my feet and able to appreciate its aesthetic qualities. The extreme calmness of the sea did not lull me into a feeling of security, for it was the swell rather than any small chop which would prostrate me. And so it did, within the first mile.

The Captain had agreed to take us over to Sula Sgeir for a short visit because I wanted to know whether the grey seals bred on the rock. There would be no seals ashore in June, of course, but if they did breed there in the autumn I should find ear bones of dead calves as evidence. This was the only chance we should have of visiting Sula Sgeir in 1939, though the swell on the sea made me more than doubtful about landing. There was another job to do there as well. James Fisher was organizing a world gannet census and had asked me to count Sula Sgeir if I possibly could. He himself hoped to go there in the ketch-rigged yacht *Escape* belonging to J. M. Robertson, when a party of bird-watchers would be making a tour of St. Kilda and other far northern gannetries.

How I cursed my seasickness that afternoon! A great hulking fellow looks so utterly shorn of any human dignity when his face is pea-green, his stomach in a state of spasm and his eyes not co-ordinating. A man cannot be right on top of his job in such a state, and to me the wonderful world of sea, cliffs and myriad birds seemed to be going on just beyond an impenetrable fence. I could see it all in a bemused way but could not feel part of it; if I could but set my feet ashore I should become a man again immediately, able to live and enjoy.

The ship stopped a quarter of a mile south of Sula Sgeir and the sickening pageant of getting the boat over the side was re-enacted. I collected my photographic gear and binoculars, or perhaps it was Bobbie who saw to it I had everything, then I recovered a little during the straight run up to the rock from the ship. There was not much white against this southern head of the rock, but a landing there would be impossible anyway, and I could see the sea rising and falling several feet against the cliff though it was not breaking.

Well, it was grand, sickness or no. That noble southern head with its crest white with guano and the great birds flying forth in thousands! I found some difficulty in making my eyes focus properly and in getting the dual images of the Leica rangefinder to come together and make one. Then we moved up to the landing place on the east side, Geodha Puill Bhain, passing the slim tunnel which the sea has made through this long, narrow islet. The sea was still rising and falling a good ten feet against those cliffs without breaking, but when we rounded a point into the eastern bay all silence of the sea was gone and we were in a seething cauldron of water which lifted and fell and broke unpredictably and very fast. The air was full of the sound of breaking water and veiled the loud cries of birds.

A bunch of twenty or thirty yearling seals basking on Thamna Sgeir fell off into the water in surprise, but again we heard no sound of their falling in the greater sound of water. We nosed as near the rocks as we could, the water working as if it were alive; foot by foot we crept along till we reached the northern point, and never a chance did we have.

The west coast of Sula Sgeir is no joke for a boat, and in this swell it was awe-inspiring. There are sunken skerries nearly all the way down, which would be invisible one moment and in the next the tangle growing on them would be lapping the gunwale. But there was something majestic in being there: a group of men and one woman were doing a good deal of what they wanted to do, undismayed and secretly enjoying it, for none had been there before. "Damn all this rock scratching" said an officer new to the service who was accustomed to the long ocean run to China and Australia, but there was a kind of incipient smile of wonder on his face all the time we were round Sula Sgeir. I thought I could climb up from the southern side of Geodha Blatha Mor where the sea seemed quietest. The launch came in for the attempt and I was poised ready to jump, but discretion kept me aboard, for the ledges were not flat enough to ensure my getting a grip. Even three or four feet of swell can upset one's timing, and I dare not risk a hundred pounds' worth of lenses and gear being immersed.

Having now sailed round the rock, it seemed worth while trying the south-east side again. We dropped an anchor astern and nosed in with engine stopped and oars out. But it was no good; the water began to boil under us and so lifted and dropped the launch that the rope entangled the propeller. Bobbie and I took a sweep apiece while the rope was freed, and we decided to give up the idea of landing. Just once more round, then, to make some estimate of the numbers of gannets. This was not easy and there were many nests on top of the rock which had to be guessed anyway. I called the number 4000 pairs.

James Fisher wrote to me later to say *Escape* had visited Sula Sgeir. He had managed to jump ashore but had had to jump back again into the dinghy immediately, with a good wetting for luck. His estimate was therefore of the same character as mine, and his figure was 3980 pairs.

As I mentioned in *Island Years* at some length, Sula Sgeir

is visited most years by a crew of men from Ness in Lewis, to get about 2000 young solans. This is the only gannetry in Britain where toll is taken of the birds, and the declining numbers show it is too heavy a toll. No authority will make any move towards some control of the numbers taken. The journey is made in an open 40-foot boat and is now somewhat in the nature of an adventurous holiday. It is indeed adventurous, for there are several records of the crew getting stranded.

Malcolm Stewart, who has himself spent two or three nights on the rock, cites a story in his book *Ronay* (Oxford, 1933) of a Ness crew being wrecked while landing on Sula Sgeir in June some time about the middle of last century. They lived on bird flesh for several weeks. The Revenue Cruiser *Prince of Wales* under Captain Oliver visited the rock in August, to find only the wreck and an old oar standing on end with a pair of canvas trousers on it. There were no men. What had happened was that a Russian ship homeward bound had taken the crew off Sula Sgeir and landed them on Rona, and it was some time before this fact was learned and the men picked up by *Prince of Wales*.

The crew of 1912 was also storm-stayed on Sula Sgeir. Here is the story as given in the *Glasgow Herald* in an anonymous note in 1939: "The boat was overtaken by a storm on the outward journey, and H.M.S. *Phoenix* went in search. She circled the island and sounded her siren and returned to report no sign of life. The men returned three weeks later to find Ness in mourning. They had been at work on the island and, according to the writer, had not noticed the *Phoenix* passing.

"But there is another story of that incident. We have it from the man who in 1912 was Free Church minister at Stornoway.

"Some time before 1830, when the French occupied Algiers, the men of Ness had sailed out into the north-west on the gannet hunt, and they did not come back. They were given up as lost, and the years passed and some of the wives remarried. Many years afterwards a ship trading on the North-West Coast of Africa sent sailors ashore for fuel and water, and in a small jungle village they came upon a community of men who spoke a strange language and observed strange customs.

"A Scotsman in the shore party identified the language as Gaelic, and it was found that these were the men who had disappeared from Lewis years before. Their boat had been captured off the Butt of Lewis by the Barbary pirates. And they had been sold into slavery.

"They were offered passage home, but refused. It was better, they said, that they should remain, for their wives might have remarried, their children would not know them, and the years of exile would have left them strangers in their own country. The trader returned with the tale, which was accepted as true. An aged member of that Free Church congregation was the son of one of the lost fishermen.

"That story was still familiar in 1912. And that was why the *Phoenix* saw no sign of life. When they returned to find Ness in mourning the gannet-hunters confessed a little shame-facedly that when they saw the *Phoenix* bear down on Sula Sgeir they remembered the story of their ancestors and the pirates, and were afraid. They took refuge in the rocks and hid themselves until they thought the coast was clear."

There is nothing to record of our voyage back to Tanera, during which I was only partly conscious anyway. We reached the Anchorage at six o'clock in the morning to give Tigsie a great surprise. And it was not long before Bobbie was talking to him like a Dutch Uncle for trying to make treacle toffee in one of her best saucepans!

Chapter 8

CALM BEFORE STORM

THERE seemed innumerable things to do when we got home from Rona, mainly concerning the second winter expedition to that island, which was to begin early in September, as soon as I could leave after the British Association Meeting at Dundee. A few loads of fencing stakes for Tigh an Quay were waiting for us near the head of Loch Broom, as well as a long thick pole which was to be made into a derrick for raising the big stones from the harbour back on to the quay. We were also expecting several lots of friends. It seemed possible—even likely—that funds would materialize for the seven years' programme of research on the migrations of the grey seals and their lines of diffusion from each breeding ground, for which work I should need a 40-foot boat of Zulu type. I went to St. Monance to see the builders of our own launch and talk over the problem. The firm built little ships of wood and the partner I met was the fifth of the line : here was no man refined by family success out of all likeness to the practical shipbuilders his forebears had been. Well educated and polished he might be, but he was in dungarees, with rules and tools in the thigh pockets of them, first and foremost a shipbuilder and man of his hands.

I enjoyed this morning in the little town of the Fife coast, watching skilled hands working on good wood, seeing a beautiful yacht taking shape. The social pattern was interesting me as much as my own enquiries about the sealing-ship. It seemed there was no depression in the building of little wooden ships, whether they were yachts or fishing-boats, and plenty of young lads were happy to come into the job. My host said he had no complaints about labour at all, the youngsters were as keen and proud to do a good job as the older men. The evidence of my own eyes bore out his statement. The sheds were full of whistling and singing, and some of the men doing delicate and difficult jobs were intently silent, completely absorbed in their work. I could not help pondering the whole scene: here were no wage-slaves, machine-minders, automata who screwed on a couple of nuts in a moving assembly line, but whole men. Everything they did was individual, they produced beautiful things and their boss was alongside them as leader and not as driver. The longer I live the more convinced I am that a man cannot achieve wholeness unless he uses his hands as well as his head. Hands are part of the quality of humanness, and their development in skills balances the tumbling, surging activity of our still young and inexperienced brain.

Then I went outside and contemplated my old Ford car to which I owed so much for its gift of mobility. Back in there I had been the sincere but doctrinaire enthusiast for the hand-made; now I was climbing into the classic example of the machine-made and I humbly remembered that if motor cars were all hand-made Rolls-Royces I should still be walking. The serious human problem remains to be solved.

Now at home, Ivan Hulburd was asking if he could not be of some use to me in my seal work with his schooner, and he was suggesting shipping Tigsie as crew. The idea suited me well, for I was anxious to map out the summer distribution of grey seals between the Summer Isles and Cape Wrath and along the North Coast. Ivan and Tigsie could take the sea way to Cape Wrath and I would go north in the Ford, working the coast and making numerous enquiries. We arranged to meet in the bay of Fiondalach Mor in Loch Laxford to compare notes, and for me to take a trip out in the schooner to outlying skerries up the coast.

This combined operation, as it would be called in the phraseology of 1942, started in all seriousness. I worked hard and gleaned a lot of useful information, and Ivan and Tigsie scoured the coasts and open Minch very well too. The trouble began on a Friday morning, and by Sunday evening the party had ceased to think of its high scientific purpose and had deteriorated to a bunch of irresponsible school kids acting the fool.

I reached the few cottages of Foindle just before noon on this lovely hot Friday in July. The sea was flat calm and unbroken by the presence of *Southseaman*. An old gentleman from one of the crofts told me she had not appeared yet, so I went back to Scourie to meet a man I had missed the day before, and to see the salmon-watcher at the foot of the Laxford River.

There were two tinkers in the river fishing for fresh-water mussels, which yield the beautiful Scottish pearls still greatly prized as jewels. These fellows had no rubber boots and did not bother to remove their shoes and socks and roll their trousers up. They went in and got wet and came out and dried without thinking any more about it. One was gathering the mussels with his right hand and holding in his other a little square box bottomed with glass which was held just below water-level to cut out reflection and distortion from the fast-moving water. The other also had his little glass box but was working in deeper water, and instead of his arm used a cleft stick for picking the mussels, which lie individually among the shingle of the river bed. It is unfortunate that a pearl-carrying mussel cannot be identified from the outside, because as so few do carry pearls there is very great wastage in opening—and killing—the mussels.

These men were as communicative as I have always found the pearl-fishing tinkers to be. Ten years earlier I had bought a lovely pearl from a tinker in Mull for half a crown, and he had carefully and accurately told me of a dry hole in which I could doss for the night, for I was at that time without a tent and sleeping rough. I have always regretted not buying from him a very large pearl which he offered me eventually for as little as five shillings. The Laxford men had a few small pink pearls in their pockets which they tried to sell me at a high price. I haggled with them for the mere fun of haggling, and as they seemed to enjoy it too I think they were well enough satisfied with three shillings for about half a dozen pearls which were either mis-shapen or too small for the jewellers. Anyway, they helpfully posed for a picture which I thought worth taking to show a Scottish rural industry which will soon be gone.

When I got back to Foindle, *Southseaman* was lying in the bay. The old gentleman had studied her lines carefully and gave me a shrewd summary of what the little schooner could and could not do. I liked this old man straight away, tall, slow, carrying his head high, and yet perfectly easy in manner. I asked if I might leave my car within his gates, and not only

XII*a*. A PEARL FISHER
AT WORK

XII*b*. THE FISHER'S CLEFT STICK

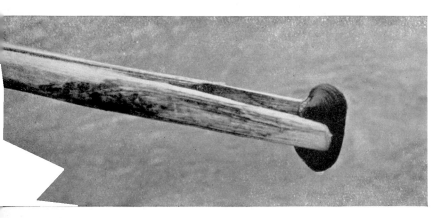

XIII. THE WEST SIDE OF SULA SGEIR

did he say yes, but invited me to take tea with him and his sister later in the day.

A high whistle from me at the shore below the crofts brought Ivan's head out of the hatch of *Southseaman* like that of a Jack-in-a-box. He waved his recognition and in a few moments Tigsie rowed ashore for me. Yes, they'd had a grand trip but hadn't seen one seal all the time. What a fine time they had had looking at the birds on the sea cliffs of Handa! I climbed aboard chattering unconcernedly, and then down through the hatch from the brilliant sunlight to the dimness of Ivan's little cabin. I have probably never been more surprised in my life, for sitting there on the lower bunks were Alec and Beryl Valentine, friends to whom I had said goodbye at Garve a week ago and whom I now thought were in London. The joke was undoubtedly on me. Alec and Beryl had decided to stay longer in the North and see Handa and Scourie again, and that is how they had struck *Southseaman*.

Well, this was the point where degeneration overtook the seal enquiries. First we had to have a meal and some tea and then go to Scourie for food for the boat party. The old gentleman at Foindle was going to walk two miles to the junction of the Lairg road to wheel home a new barrow, but I managed to save him this journey with no more fuss than his sister making him change into a pair of shining black boots before he stepped into my car—the old Ford of many a rough trip, which was cleaned once a year whether it wanted it or not! Little as I would have wished him to change into those boots, I accepted the gesture as one which is typical of the unspoilt Gael who wishes to do you honour. I remember another occasion, during that old-style and famous Ross and Cromarty by-election of 1936, when an oblique but none the less sure compliment was paid me by an independent, hard-drinking lady of a neighbouring crofting township. My car was taking a load eight miles to the polling booth, the woman sitting by me and three crofters crushed in the back seats. She drew forth a packet of cigarettes, picked out one at a time and handed them over her shoulders to the men in the back. Then she offered the packet to me to take one myself.

It began to rain and blow from the south-west that evening

G

after a long spell of dry weather. The prospect of sailing up
the North Minch to Cape Wrath and back on the morrow was
no treat to me as I lay curled up in the back of my car, the
sound of the rain accentuated as it drove against the hood and
found its way inside. I knew the rain had come to stay this
time, and in fact it did not stop for the next thirty-six hours.
Burns were running well as I went to the shore to go aboard
Southseaman. My innermost feelings were disconsolate compared with the hilarious state in which I found the boat party;
after all, it was fun to them whatever happened, but I was
locating seals as a job of work. The rain dripped down inside
the collar of my oilskin and through the bulky green cotton
neckerchief I wear on such occasions. The islands of Loch
Laxford did not look exciting from the point of view of seeing
birds, though I noticed several small heronries with youngsters
where I could have got good photographs easily.

Chug, chug, chug went the Diesel engine as we almost
headed into the wind; and we got wetter and wetter. Rain
with plenty of action can be a pleasant thing, but to have to
stand around in it and get cold is deadening to the spirits. Alec
was quiet and Tigsie laconic but secretly very happy: Ivan
and Beryl got more and more cheerful as we reached the open
sea where the engine could be stopped and sails raised, for these
two were sailors for the love of it.

The scene which would have been glorious to me from the
top of a cliff became a wretched moving greyness as we rolled
and weaved through a bigger sea than the wind merited. There
was no hope of seeing or counting seals in this, or of poking
a boat close in to the skerries I wished to examine. However,
I had come a good way to do the work and Ivan had put his
little ship at my disposal, so onward I preferred to go, feeling
like death. We saw no seals at all on or near the skerries where
I thought they might be. The weather was getting worse
rather than better, and, trying my best to dissociate the feeling
and desires occasioned by the state of my stomach from what
scientific detachment demanded, I came to the conclusion it
was better to call it a day and return to Loch Laxford.

I felt as bright as could be as soon as we dropped anchor
and began to prepare a meal, and after that I played the mouth-

organ for a singsong which went well with Ivan's voice leading the choruses and his hand conducting. Such exercise of five pairs of lungs in a small cabin over which the hatch has been drawn to keep out the rain caused a unanimous demand for air. We went ashore in *Southseaman's* little tender the *Atoll*, Alec to poach a couple of lochs—though he knew quite well it was no fishing day, Ivan and Tigsie to walk through that queer country of rocky knolls, and Beryl and I to go through to the south side of the peninsula and to Scourie for some more shopping. Seals being off, we were enjoying the picnic as such.

My hosts at Foindle asked me in for the evening and would not hear of my sleeping in my car that night. How much I enjoyed our quiet conversation of homely things, sitting comfortably on the settle, getting a whiff of peat smoke from time to time and hearing the kettle sing for another drink of tea. For me this evening had the spice of contrast with our ribald idiocy during the day. And not least did I enjoy the Gaelic prayers which my host read last thing in his deep and beautifully modulated voice.

It was still raining the following morning and Beryl's car would not start. Tigsie took charge, cleaned the plugs, pointed to a cracked bakelite plug lead, adjusted the points and generally fiddled as mechanics do. But the car would not start. Your expert is always so academic. I knew that all the car needed was a good shove forward in second gear, for I have had cars get wet in the rain many a time, but it seemed a point of honour with Tigsie that she must start from standstill. There were four of us to shove, and by now two or three men from the crofts close by had joined the party. My counsel prevailed at last, and of course the car went away with no further trouble.

I was a little anxious this morning because it was the Sabbath and we seemed to be creating rather a hubbub in the devout atmosphere of Foindle, but I felt I had managed the situation rather well when my host and hostess accepted my invitation for them to ride in my car to church at Scourie, nearly six miles away. I admired their tolerance and beautiful courtesy in face of a bunch of incomers, some of whom were so incurably cheerful, and I was led to reflect on a problem which exercises my mind more and more—that of the behaviour of the individual and of people acting as a community. The exceedingly narrow Presbyterianism of the North-West would have damned us out and out, yet these two old folk who were practising members could not have been kinder and more forbearing to us who were disturbing their holy day. I should have gone away uneasy if they had declined to ride into Scourie, and I perfectly understood when they asked to be set down a quarter of a mile this side of the church.

Beryl and Alec were waiting for me on the north side of Kylesku Ferry, for we had decided to spend the afternoon walking high into the grand country north of Loch Glen Coul. How much I enjoyed it! My mind was sated with island coasts and sea for the time being and I wanted the beauty of the glens and the high hill. We came on plenty of deer, found a black-throated diver's nest, and I was struck by the richness of the flora here compared with that of the Torridonian Sandstone of Tanera and the adjacent mainland. From the hill I saw the big yacht *Norseman* steam up Loch Glen Coul with half her square sails set. The last time I had seen her was in Oban Bay in 1937 when we had come back from Iona before going to the Treshnish Isles.

My friends were starting their run back to London this Sunday evening, so we thought a quiet tea at Kylesku Hotel would be a good farewell. But this was not to be: the brown sails and green hull of *Southseaman* sailed into the anchorage from Loch Cairnbaun and we knew the chances of a quiet meal were few. Ivan's bellow of a laugh set us all going and Tigsie seemed to drop his reserve and become frisky. We ate an enormous tea, everybody's wit seemed sharpened and we laughed so much that Tigsie finished on the floor. Here were five well-brought-up and normally well-behaved people, ranging in age from twenty-six to forty, acting like a lot of kids at a bun-fight or undergraduates in a teashop—and on the Highland Sabbath at that.

Next day Ivan, Tigsie and I sailed up to the head of Loch Glen Coul. It is a beautiful and remote place, the hills rocky and varied in line, the slopes lightly flecked with birches and the red July coats of the deer standing out from the new green of the high ground. I half envied the stalker who lived at the head of the loch with his well-built little house and nice bit of arable ground. He told me of the pine martens in the cairns of rocks close by and I was tempted to stay up there for a night or two to see them for myself, because I have never seen more than the tail end of a pine marten disappearing into some small trees.

This was the end of our trip. I hurried home to get on with some work and to enjoy the company of more friends who had come to see us. There was Margaret Stewart, lover of little children, who, born in Labrador and reared in China, had travelled across Siberia as a child in the last war; there was Archie Leggate, surgeon, physician and saint, son of a family devoted to the service of their fellow-men; and Ted Fynn, *quondam* Rhodes Scholar, a man with a gift for human contacts and having a deep social conscience. I hardly know when we slept, for there were the days to enjoy among the islands and the nights for good talk. One night I was playing the mouth-organ while Bobbie, Margaret, Ted and Archie were dancing in the schoolroom of the house on Tanera and it seemed to me we were snatching golden moments of a precarious peace from which the sands were fast running out. "Play on, play on, and keep them dancing," said the gnome inside me; "this party will never meet again."

I used to come back to the fruitless subject of war time and again in our conversation. What was our intellectual attitude and what would our actual behaviour be? It really was fruitless because we could be only academic and ignorant of our destiny. Since then, our dear Archie has gone; he was last seen moving among the wounded men on the deck of a sinking destroyer, giving his all to those lost men as he gave his all in the slums of Liverpool. Ted Fynn has gone from our ken; the last we heard of him he was in an anti-aircraft battery as a private, enjoying equality with working lads; and here am I still on Tanera, a fact which three years ago I should have thought impossible in the circumstances of war.

The summer of 1939 is one we shall remember as a happy one. We seemed to play hard as well as getting a lot of work done. Visitors were numerous, some coming to stay with us and others calling casually from yachts which used the Anchorage, or rowing over from the mainland. There was a grand day when a party from Stowe School called and which gave me the idea that visits of small groups from schools might be developed, for in the new world we are to make the Highlands must not remain a rich man's playground only, but a training ground for youngsters in roughing it as well.

Our company began to melt away in August. Ivan set sail for Shetland in *Southseaman*, Tigsie went to Switzerland to climb, and we to Edinburgh and Berwick, at which latter place I was to study the grey seal problem in relation to the salmon-fishery of the Tweed Estuary. I was looking forward to seeing the isolated group of these seals on the Farne Islands.

Then Bobbie and I were going on to Dundee for the Meeting of the British Association. Whatever clouds were gathering outside, our own little world was a very happy one at that time.

Chapter 9

MAINLY POLITICAL

BOBBIE and I lived in College at St. Andrews for the Dundee Meeting of the British Association, leaving the Ford in Dundee and travelling to and fro across the Tay by rail. We met Dick Purchon, a Bristol zoologist, in the train and shared the delight of going from the station to the College in an open growler. It was grand; we had not been in a carriage since childhood, and Purchon was too young to have known them in general use. We came to know this young man as having the rare gift of making intensely interesting an account of the mouth parts of an obscure marine invertebrate, and as I listened to him I hoped sincerely he would soon get a lecturer's post. But war has overtaken him too and he is in a German prison camp.

War was in the air and everyone silently apprehensive; it seemed wrong to me then to calmly assume war was inevitable, because every thought and action of us, the common folk, should be to prevent war occurring through over-excitement. I thought then that Germany would come to the very brink of war but would not be foolish enough to precipitate it. I passionately believed peace could be kept at that moment and that we should use the peace immediately to get together a new round table of nations. I was wrong, of course; our back-sliding had been so consistent in the past that the enemy was scarcely to be blamed for expecting further concession; now, the attack on Poland showed the insensate lust of Nazi Germany and the power the regime had over the people. Perhaps this passionate belief of mine was a defence put up by the mind to cover the clear vision I had of what war would mean.

The reception given by the Lord Provost of Dundee in the Caird Hall was a brilliant affair. Scarlet academic gowns and brightly coloured women's dresses, tables well loaded with good food, the strains of the orchestra and the movement of the dance—I found myself wondering if it was real. Was this

103

another ball of the eve of Waterloo? Well, the lamps of Europe went out in a gay and happy moment of our two lives. A meeting of the "British Ass." is an interesting phenomenon to the social observer; you see men of science like a lot of children at school, going into their various classes and trying to be serious, but as soon as they are let out they romp joyfully into the tea-rooms, into the general office where an indulgent secretariat is kind to them all, and off they go in charabancs for afternoon treats which are called "geological excursion" and "visit to the soap works". The town chosen for the Meeting is always kind to the men of science in giving them a reception, a dance, a feed and a garden party. No one should get the idea there is anything fusty about a British Ass. Meeting. Scientists are at play, thoroughly enjoying themselves and laughing nearly all the time. They like going about in their old straw boaters and open-necked shirts, just as much as they do dressing up in scarlet gowns and ornamental hoods for the evening functions. There is a small faction in science which professes itself superior to this mediaeval play-acting of gowns and biretta, but its members show a lack of wisdom. It does us good to dress up sometimes, and just as display among birds produces and synchronizes an emotional state in a flock, so does the panoply of these gatherings invest them with a dignity and beauty felt throughout the company.

I shall never forget the following day. There were no morning news broadcasts then, so we went to our sectional meetings unknowing. But in the middle of the morning I went up to the B.B.C. room to make final arrangements about an evening broadcast I was to give. Ian Cox told me the news, and while I sat there sipping sherry with him fresh news was coming all the time of the German advance into Poland. I made some rather foolish remarks to Cox to the effect that I hoped we should not invade German territory and put ourselves on their level, but fight them back to their own frontier. He exploded this momentary confusion completely by asking me how I thought we were going to get to Poland to fight. How on earth did the Chamberlain Government think we were going to *defend* Poland either? They had boggled at the tardy truth of saying that if Germany marched into Poland we should

attack Germany. It had always been the language of politicians
and newspapers that Britain's declaring war on Germany was
"unthinkable", but the eventual situation was so contrived that
we did declare war and attack German territory, though in
what half-hearted fashion we now know all too well.

I said goodbye to Cox, whose careful preparatory work for
this week of broadcasts from the Meeting had been rendered
fruitless. Down in the General Office the news was filtering
in; the secretaries were obviously troubled men, members'
faces were grave and I saw one girl, wearing the red gown of
a St. Andrews undergraduate, standing with her eyes looking
far into the future. There was no fear there, but the same tragic
clarity of vision I knew so well. We spoke together for a while,
two sorrowing folk without hate in our hearts, both with a
sense of outraged honour through the behaviour of this country's
leaders, wondering how it was that such a small group of men
in Europe could so grossly misrepresent the kindly heart and
the honour of simple and lowly folk.

Then Bobbie came in and the mood was gone in the urgency
of practical detail. Alasdair was in Edinburgh and we must
relieve his hosts of their responsibility. Until an official statement should cancel the Meeting, we must continue to stay by
the Association and attend the sessions. And so we went into
lunch, which was a busy meal we did not enjoy. I felt sorry
for our guest, for none of us was on top of conversational form,
the runner beans were wretchedly stringy and the mutton fat
and tough and barely warm. Then a fellow I knew from the
British Museum who had just got to Dundee from London
came and sat with us. A night journey in a British train in
summer is sufficiently enervating of itself, but to have come
merely to return again immediately, and because of such news,
was enough to take the sparkle out of him. A famous physiologist
was sitting by himself two tables away from us; white-haired,
fine-featured, with his chin resting on his chest as his eyes looked
out beyond this eating place altogether, and his meal was
untouched. The sorrow in that man's face stuck in my mind's
eye during the next few days as typical of the feelings of almost
everybody I met. There was no anger, only sorrow.

We went in the afternoon to a film of the grey seal, a com-

mentary being given by R. H. Hewer, the Recorder of the
Zoology Section. He mentioned that Dr. Fraser Darling would
be giving a lecture on this animal on the following Tuesday
afternoon; it was a brave gesture, for I am sure all of us in
that darkened room knew we should not be gathered there
four days hence. When we came out from the film show a
blackboard notice in the General Office proclaimed that the
remainder of the Meeting was cancelled, and in such an
atmosphere of anti-climax everyone was trying decently to say
goodbye and disappear.

Bobbie and I drove to Edinburgh as fast as we could via
Queensferry, and were warned we should have to dim our
lights if we were to drive in the dark. A long string of cars
was waiting at the Ferry, but we did not have to wait long
before going aboard, and there was plenty to interest us anyway.
It was a dull evening of poor visibility, making the destroyers
and cruisers then passing down the Forth into impersonal,
mysterious silhouettes. They were moving out to the North
Sea, where who knew what adventures would be awaiting
them. A number of blue-globed hurricane lamps were standing
on the deck of the ferry-boat, and seeing my interest in them
a deck-hand picked one up to show me:

"And what do you think?" he said in a voice expressing
both amusement and exasperation. "The bloody things were
made in Germany!"

It is indeed a wonder that that ingenious nation did not peddle
gas masks, stirrup pumps and cut-price black-out material
throughout this country and threatened Europe.

We were soon in Edinburgh and back on the road again to
the Ferry with Alasdair between Bobbie and me in the front
of the car. It was lighting-up time soon after our second
crossing, and as black-out restrictions were in force we had
to drive on the sidelights, which a policeman told us were still
a bit too bright. Bobbie had the brilliant idea of smearing
the lenses with face-cream, a device which was entirely successful.

We left the grey and lovely old town early in the morning,
saying a sad goodbye to our friends of the British Ass. and to
Alasdair's hosts of the night. Then our nose was pointed
northwards and home, which we reached that evening, 2nd

September. All along our route we had struck that sadness and sorrow which was devoid of hate and vindictiveness. It was as typical of the common folk as of the academic gathering.

The following day was for us what it must have been for most people—uncertainty, gloom, resignation to the inevitable.

War grieved me more than anything else has ever done. All I could see at that time was a crash of our struggling efforts at social reform, a throwing away of over twenty years, a stagnation for how many more, and I felt an exasperation at those old men who had brought the nation step by step along the path of shame. I was one of those who had supported the National Government in its early years, little realizing that the system held the seeds of parliamentary decay, and like most others I had not been wide awake enough in 1931 to see the devastation wrought by our indifferent attitude to Japan. When the Wal Wal incident was mentioned on the wireless I knew it was the spark of long and serious trouble, but I did not doubt for one moment that Britain would lead the League of Nations and that Italy would be dissuaded from aggression. That was what we stood for, I thought. But I did not know the quality of the men who could rat down any hole which led away from firmness. Sir Samuel Hoare's speech to the League in September 1935 was magnificent; it was the true voice of the people of Britain. How could we know then that this same man three months later would come to an understanding with the man who was to be known as the dirtiest politician in Europe? This most disreputable incident in the history of the National Government came after a General Election fought on the issue of adherence to League principles, and in which election well over 400 supporters were returned to the House, most of them Conservatives. The people of Britain were of one opinion in this matter and elected their representatives because they professed the same faith. Step by step our faith was shattered. The imposition of sanctions on Italy might have been designed for failure, because the sanctions were on those commodities consumed by the common folk who were not the cause of the trouble. The only embargoes justified in such instances of aggression are those which would affect war supplies, namely, metals and oil. The National Government of Great Britain and the United States have always skated round this obvious point, for adherence to such a principle would have affected pockets.

I have never been able to understand the British Government's behaviour in the Abyssinian affair, even on the grounds of expediency. Our betrayal of principle gravely injured our name throughout Africa, and especially in those areas like Nigeria and the Gold Coast where we have educated the African to take part in government on European lines. The Government's glib excuse that it was not Britain that failed Abyssinia but the League, and that Britain was not the League, was just plain havers. Britain *was* the League to the extent that that body could not stand without her and that Britain's firmness and loyalty were the requirement of world opposition to aggression. Even the lack of sympathy and cohesion between Britain and France was insufficient reason for our backsliding.

Then came the Spanish Civil War with the British Government's masterly manipulation of the League to achieve nullity with the greatest possible amount of verbiage. I am not prepared to argue the rights and wrongs of either side in the Spanish War, but like most other people I was inflamed by the inexpedience of our actions which gave Italy and Germany the opportunity to whittle away what little strength we had. Mr. Baldwin was a man of dexterity in home affairs, and in justice to that astute man I do not think he had any inflated notions of his ability in the foreign field. But the advent of Mr. Neville Chamberlain as prime minister catapulted us along a new course of international ruin. This man *thought* he knew how to manage affairs and acted with all the assured self-confidence of the man of little experience.

By the spring of 1937 I was disillusioned and bitter and ashamed of my own country, a state which I found to be shared by nearly all my contemporaries. The Government was a body of old men and reactionaries, the latter taking advantage of the tiredness and tendency to seek the easiest way so evident in the former. From this time onwards Britain was losing her democracy and her strength of parliamentary government. I, who was reared in and had followed true-blue Toryism, grew

disgusted with the unbridled power of that party and its exercise
of it, and turned away searching for a new label which was
difficult to find. The Liberals seemed to me an ineffectual
group split within themselves; and how could I tack myself
on to Labour, a party which ruled its members through trade-
union dictatorship and which did not denounce the horrible
doctrine of class war? The honest man of science is hard set
in the field of politics, yet I feel that scientific men must put
aside their personal diffidence and be prepared to take their
place in parliamentary government. It was at this time I became
Winston Churchill's man and suffered a good deal of ridicule
for my admiration of him.

I remember the reproof and ostracism I received during an
evening with some University colleagues when I plainly voiced
my opinion of the British Government to a foreigner. A Czech
visitor was showing me some photographs of his country and
I could see the man's pride in it.

"Are you not afraid of Hitler?" I asked.

"Oh no, not really," he said, "because we know that Great
Britain could never allow Germany to take our country. Mind
you, we do not think of that as pure unselfishness on Britain's
part, but that she would not be so foolish as to let it happen."

"Then the sooner you change your notions the better," I
said, "for I am pretty sure that the present British Government
will rat down every hole till the last, and when it does reach
that last corner from which there is no further retreat, it will
turn to fight with a pious cry about defending freedom."

And so we went on: the policy of rearmament was accepted
but not executed; Mr. Chamberlain went to Rome and
sedulously excluded Mr. Churchill from the Government.
Whatever I may think of the Government, it remains my
firm belief that Mr. Chamberlain was an honest man. But
honesty in no way excuses his stupidity and his flair for
picking second-raters. His stupidity did not cease with the
outbreak of war, rather did it wax until the famous speech
at Birmingham when he proclaimed that Hitler had "missed
the 'bus". The news bulletins were still telling us that Saarbrücken was ready to fall "like a ripe plum" whenever Allied
strategy should decide it.

My resentment rose steadily while I girned at the impotence felt by myself and so many others. My spirits fell because I could not see how we were to rid ourselves of these men. Then came the change of 10th May, 1940, and all was different. I had underestimated the power of Parliament in British life, but this overthrow of a despised and mistrusted ministry gave me back my faith. When Mr. Chamberlain broadcast his resignation and announced Mr. Churchill as prime minister I silently saluted him, for in his going he rose to great heights. It had been the practice to excuse Mr. Chamberlain's misdirection of affairs on the grounds of his complete honesty and the goodness of his intentions. All this I accept, but not as an excuse : if a manager of a business brings it to the verge of ruin he is heaved out immediately and honesty and good intentions will not keep him his job.

The appointment of Mr. Churchill as prime minister altered my outlook on the war, because I could be whole-hearted about it now. The insincerity of the previous eight months and the earlier backsliding had made me feel there was no reason for the continuance of war on these lines. I thought in the early months that the world could have got together in conference and made peace by Germany relinquishing her conquests in the face of united world opinion. It is most probable that I was entirely wrong and misjudging the widespread desire for military victory and the high morale in Germany.

International events are hardly ever what they seem. The Russian actions in Poland and the Baltic States struck me as revolting, and though I now see the expediency of Russia's action, I cannot agree that she was anything but clumsy. The outbreak of the Russo-Finnish War appeared a clear-cut issue for freedom, and I should undoubtedly have gone to fight there had I not suffered an accident later to be mentioned. Of course, we see now that I was wrong again ; it was no clear-cut issue for freedom at all, but a necessary action on Russia's part for her own protection. But I still deplore the way Russia went to work and I remain an admirer of the magnificent Finnish resistance during those three and a half months.

The war has been full of surprises and of examples of the fallibility of human reasoning. We who are the common folk have found our reasoning to be based on shifting sands of unsound premises, the very realization of which has given us a determination towards political consciousness. The people of Britain will not lapse into inertia again after this war, and the sooner the high Tories understand this, the better it will be for all of us. The forces of the Right can put forward a most plausible case: their honest wish is to raise the standard of living of the masses, and to provide the people with the goods they desire. But when thoroughly examined in the light of such Tory productions as the party's report on education and the Scott Report on land utilization, we see that the Right wishes to create a well-fed and obedient commonalty which will work the machinery of production and provide a market for the products of industry. The people will be given that which the Right thinks to be good for them; pleasures there will be in plenty, for have not the dazzling foyers of luxury cinemas already shown their value as soporifics? And such things pay. The pleasures a man finds and makes for himself are no good to the investor.

Let us get this straight: if the masses want ease after this war they can get it. Big business will supply it as a matter of policy, lots and lots of beer and cigarettes. Even in the throes of total war we see that brewers' profits are safe and their company reports record high-minded self-congratulation on their part in maintaining morale. There will be the same profession of service to the people in peace-time, and the people may be hoodwinked very easily by the brightness of pleasures which are like the decorations of a Christmas tree. The Labour Party, weighted so heavily with trade-union representatives, also clamours and promises about the very things the Right is so anxious to supply. Both parties are in effect saying to the people, "You want ease and pleasure; we can give it you."

As it seems to me, we need a great change of mind throughout our people, less of a desire to get and more of a notion of giving to the community. Most of us can be generous to those we love and know; the test comes in serving and giving to those we do not know. To render operative the recommendations of a Beveridge Report is a duty of the country as a whole, but equally it is the duty of every man and woman to accept social security as something which can be upheld only by their own service to the community. Giving service is not generally easy, it often means going without and being satisfied with one's own effort for little pleasures and comforts. In all that we think should be done for us with the resources in the hands of a Government, there is also our personal and individual contribution to be made. We need eager, eager work, undertaken in a spirit that we ourselves may not reap the full reward but that posterity may. Free beer and luxury models have no place in the toil we must put forth in building our new life, in which unselfish toil there seem to me such opportunities of joy as we have never known in this century.

XIV. ATLANTIC GREY SEALS BASKING ON LISGEIR MHOR, NORTH RONA

XV. POLL THOTHATOM, NORTH RONA
showing ledges of nesting seabirds

Chapter 10

THE CHANGED LIFE

THE advent of war taught us much. We found our normal life and means cut from beneath our feet and it did not seem to matter at all. I hardly felt regret for the loss of the research I had hoped to do and which enthusiasm of years had built up. Grief enveloped me; grief, not gloom or anger. Perhaps I was slightly bitter a little later on when I found that a man of thirty-six was a young man no more and not immediately required for service if he had had no previous military training. Worse still, the kind of knowledge I had seemed to be of no value, even my agricultural knowledge, which was probably deeper and sounder than in the wider field of biology in which I had delved of recent years.

It so happened that we went back from the thrilling world of science as displayed in the British Association Meeting to the simple tasks of primitive harvesting. Our friend Donnie Fraser, Raon Mor, had gone to Rhodesia, the young men of Achiltibuie were mostly away to join their units of the Seaforths, and Donnie's mother's harvest needed cutting. The house was full of grandchildren, buzzing with happiness which no war could dull as yet. Some of these grandchildren had been born in Peru, and their mother, the wife of a Scottish medical missionary, had travelled far from the mode of life of the croft.

I look back on that week or two of glorious September weather as a good memory. Bobbie and I went over in the dinghy nearly every day with Alasdair, who joined the pack of youngsters. They all looked alike in their tattered kilts and the varied backgrounds of their lives were hidden. They were a bunch of Highland children barefoot and free in an environment in which their forebears far and near had been reared. It was little different among us who were grown up. The erstwhile man of science took up his scythe and stone and mowed into the field of oats. His own wife and the wife of the medical missionary bent their backs to gather the corn into sheaves, and their fingers tied the sheaves with a bond of straw. The movements of the hands in tying that bond had come back to them over long years of disuse, sure and unforgotten.

We were peasant folk again doing first things.

The children helped a little, but not much, for the concentration was not to be expected for long. The happy laughter was a joyous sound of the harvest-field. Yonder sat Mrs. Fraser herself on her low chair, joyful in that which she knew: one baby on her wide lap, another clinging to her knee as it made experimental steps, and the golden corn was all about in a golden air. As I straightened my back to sharpen the scythe I would look to where she sat, a Ceres who is ageless and of all time. Not one of us there who did not bow to her greatness, knowing or unknowing.

The corn fell under my scythe and rose again in stooks of ten sheaves each. The sun shone, the straw dried and the harvest was carried. The mood was gone.

So Bobbie and I turned to the ruin of Tanera, where from decay and degradation we might build when destruction in the outer world seemed imminent. There was no half-heartedness or regret in this decision for such time as we might be able to pursue it. The stone quay which might be so beautiful and which would be invaluable in working the place as a home and farm was still an eyesore, a tumble of great boulders left by past gales and those human crows who came forty years before to steal the dressed Caithness stones.

No work could have been better than this for helping to rearrange the mind at such a time. Stone is of the stuff of beauty. How often have I gazed at the varying structure of the millstone grit which together with the mountain limestone of northern dales was the stone of my boyhood! The shine of tiny crystals, the cleanness of newly broken stone, the strata of colour and texture in each stone, and finally this beauty of colour and crystal blended by men's hands in a well-built dyke of dry-stone, or a house built of it and roofed with slabs of sandstone. That gritstone of my youth cut clean and some of it split well along the strata: the limestone of the dales hard by was different, breaking into hard jagged lumps which needed a wholly different handling to build it into a dry-stone dyke.

But it remained interesting because it was difficult, and in the pale grey stone itself were fossils of an early world of which I had then newly become conscious.

The Torridonian Sandstone of Tanera is red, dotted with tiny cornelians and uncertain in its break and split. It looks well newly built, but never harmonizes with the landscape like the browns of the gritstone. Our ruin is built wholly of Torridonian stone, some of it pale red and irregular, some the colour of port wine, closely and evenly stratified and easy to dress. These darker stones appear mostly at the corners, door jambs and windows, and there are several in the pier, though a black lichen has there overspread them like paint, masking their beauty.

The rough blocks littering the quay were shifted back into place with crowbar and by sheer strength. You work slowly with big stone; slow steady movements and the weight of your body move the stones a few inches or an inch until they find their niche and are chocked. Sometimes stone strikes stone, a spark flies, there is a flick of blue, blue smoke and the air fills with the clean smell of that moment of heat.

We made a stone-barrow of battens of wood which had encased the huts we had on Rona; it was a job of a few minutes only to make that simple, useful tool, and now, over three years later, it is still in use, having carried hundreds of tons of stone between the toughened bodies of Bobbie and myself. I lay the barrow flat near the stone, I roll its one or two hundred-weights on to the slatted face of the barrow; we stand one at each end, each one's feet close beneath the body, we bend low and take each our pair of handles and wait for the word "Right" from each of us before we lift the barrow. Bobbie moves forward with her left foot first, I with my right, and so does another stone travel its hundred, its eighty or fifty yards along the quay to reach a place we hope it will keep for many a long year.

We also rigged the derrick, a twenty-foot pole of Scots pine carrying four stout rope guys at its head, each one ten fathoms long. The derrick moved a few feet at a time with the course of the work, its foot buried in the gravel of the harbour or in the coarser stone outside the quay, the free ends of the guys tied north, south, east and west, each to a great boulder, over which we piled more boulders until it was possible for a man to swarm up the guys without the head of that derrick swaying, or wrenching the opposite guy from its hold. When the derrick was as sound as that we would hang the endless chain block and tackle to its head and we were ready again to lift the large blocks of stone from the harbour.

Slow, slow work it was down there, for the tide would cover that part of the harbour for several hours of the day. Our rhythm of work followed the daily lag of the tide, so that we would be working sometimes when darkness was upon us or the tide itself washing around our legs and bidding us be gone for the day. Bobbie would be on the quay running down the block till it reached the floor of the harbour; I would be slipping a chain under a boulder or dressed block of stone and making the tie fast; I would take the hook of the block, fasten it with a simple turn to the chain in my other hand, and I would call on Bobbie to haul gently. The stone would leave its old bed in the gravel and come to the foot of the pole, and where it had lain a strange fauna of darkness would writhe in an agony of disturbance—red lobworms, tiny red-and-white-striped crabs, apparently inert blobs of jelly, and sometimes, if the stone were not too deeply set, a little dancing fish called a *cuilleach* in the Gaelic: dancing himself out of sight, in contrast with the eels which glided away so smoothly.

Then Bobbie would lower the block a few inches for me to take up the slack in the chain so that the next vertical haul would see the stone level with the surface at which we were working. It was now my turn to haul, for the vertical lift needed a greater strength than Bobbie's, though sometimes a big stone would need everything the two of us could do on that endless chain. Inch by inch the stone would rise till it cleared the level of the quay; Bobbie would pull inwards on it while I quickly lowered the block, and there the stone lay on the quay once more, waiting to be levered to its place. The chain and salt water were hard on our hands, as were the stones themselves. All papillation was worn from the pads of our fingers till the blood showed a bright pink through the thinness of skin, and when we came in at night we would have to be careful of picking up hot things, so immediate was the transmission through our fingers.

But peace came in through the finger-tips as well, from that touch of the stone as we fitted it to its appointed place and found it good and firm. There is a great peace to be got from hands in use; the control of tools and of big things like these boulders was a co-ordination which reached the whole man in us.

Nightly we walked home slowly to the schoolhouse on the cliff half a mile away. Then I would take a crock and go down to Ard-na-goine to milk a couple of pints from a little black cow. She was almost dry, but her half-gallon of milk a day made her worth the small rent which we paid our neighbour for her. She grazed with the other rough cattle, and as there was no byre or place to tie her (and she, though quiet enough, not disposed to stand for long) I would milk her with my right hand and hold the crock in my left, Highland fashion.

I love drawing milk through my fingers and hearing the sound of it piercing the mounting foam in crock or pail. And here on Ard-na-goine, with the sea plashing on either side and the mountains darkening into the night, milking the little black cow was a moment of joy in my day and war was forgotten. There was the distant calling of the barnacle geese newly come to this green point, there were the near sounds of rough tongues licking backs on which the hair was growing long for the winter, of diligent muzzles plucking the grass, and if they were not grazing I would hear the soft, rhythmic cudding of the cattle, together with the comfortable rumblings of their vast bellies. How long, I wondered, would this go on?

Autumn is usually heralded on the West Highland coast by a south-easterly gale which comes with extraordinary suddenness and blows with great intensity for a long time. When it came in this year of 1939 on 8th October it was our first experience of it on Tanera, where its results were far more striking than on other and wilder islands where we have spent the autumn. All summer growth withers in a night and the leaves are gone from the few little trees before they have reached the glory of autumnal colouring. That gale came before we were satisfied about the safety of the launch, and showed us an Anchorage of Tanera which could be inhospitable.

The real suffering was in the house we lived in. I have described the course of south-easterly gales in *Island Years* when we had only tents or little huts for shelter. But we never suffered the hardship we did in this stone house on the cliff top. Its shoddy doors let in the wind, the sashes rattled and the noise of wind everywhere was hell. We endured a week of this big gale in growing discomfort; then it calmed suddenly for half a day, long enough for us to get a mail and to breathe in our lungsful of sweet air again. I also discovered my throat was sore.

The gale was blowing as hard as ever by nightfall and continued for another week. My sore throat developed into a quinsy. I have an almost Erewhonian shame of that kind of illness, for a quinsy is in the nature of dirt, coming upon a lowered system. Who was I to have such a weakness, I who had such advantages in way of life and bodily strength? I was laid very low by that quinsy, and by the continuance of that dreadful south-easterly wind.

But at least Bobbie and I realized this, that we would not live in that house even if it were offered to us rent free. We designed a little house of wood on the lines of our earlier island huts, but with three rooms instead of one. At least, we thought, it would do for the period of the war until we could think about rebuilding Tigh an Quay. We imagined standing on the Planestones facing the quay and it seemed an ideal very far away. Ideals come true by action, so the first mail out placed our design before our old friends Messrs. Cowiesons in Glasgow and asked for their quotation. It came in due course and was accepted immediately, after which we had to wait patiently for about thirty sections and various bales of oddments to come to Badentarbet by steamer.

My whole being rebelled and was humbled by the weakness in which the quinsy left me for a week or two. I carried on with work on the quay as hard as I could because I was too proud to be weak. Margaret Leigh, author of *Highland Homespun*, came to us for a visit at this time and worked just as hard as we did on that quay, carting and carrying the seemingly endless loads of stone needed for the ever-yawning maw of the quay. There was the parapet also, which I was building close on the heels of the main construction as I reached the final level.

That parapet is built in dry-stone. It would have to be very strong to withstand easterly gales and it would in a measure be carrying my reputation. Already we had been told the first winter's gales would destroy our work and that it was not to be expected the limited work a man and a woman alone could do would stand. The parapet was five feet wide at the level of the quay and tapered to two feet at the top. Every outer stone needed wedging from within, most carefully, and the middle of the parapet was closely packed with small stones, barrow after barrow of them. When I was a lad the old dry-stone dyker who taught me how to build constantly reiterated the axiom "You must keep your middle well filled." It was I then who was doing the boring job of gathering small stones.

We carried on. Margaret and I would be down on the job early and Bobbie would follow soon, bringing a picnic lunch and a primus stove for plenty of hot tea. We saw that quay growing clean before our eyes and were happy altogether. Each night going up the cliff again our eyes would glance back along the extending line of the parapet, straight and good and clean.

It is a custom in the Highlands to belittle the work of women in certain fields. Why, I cannot think, for they do a great deal. Women manage the cows and work at the peats, at the potatoes—both planting and lifting—and at harvest. But the Highlander cannot imagine a woman as being any good with sheep, with boats or in constructive work. But there were Margaret Leigh and Bobbie and I getting on with something big and heavy. The satisfaction of looking at the quay was enhanced when we laid a heavy two-point chain mooring for the launch just off the quay. Laying a mooring is a heavy job for all concerned, but these two women and I managed it perfectly. I had built a framework in the stern of the dinghy, over which I could run the heavy chain. Bobbie and Margaret were at the oars and pulled me and the anchors and chains just where I wanted. The launch could now lie safe for the winter, and as events proved, I was only just in time with this irksome job which I had had to force myself to do.

We had by this time become the proud possessors of a small flock of Shetland sheep. It is one thing buying sheep, but a very different one getting them where you want them. Ours were to go on Eilean a' Chleirich, which we had been able to rent as an addition to our small Tanera property, and were to be fetched from Poolewe. This meant taking our launch the ten miles to Gruinard, spending the night there with a friend, taking the car which he kindly offered us and going two journeys of fourteen miles to fetch the sheep on the following day. It was a very great act of friendship to lend a man a car for such a purpose, for the carriage of twenty-one sheep made it into an indescribable mess and there was no time to clean the car once we had got the sheep down into the launch.

I have always loved Shetland sheep since I first worked with them in 1928 at the Institute of Animal Genetics in Edinburgh. They have wisdom which other sheep have lost; they have primitive grace and their soft chestnut-coloured "moorit" wool gives them a most satisfying appearance. Then I saw much of them in Shetland in 1929, and as a result of that visit my friend Dr. Edmonston Saxby gave to the Institute one of the best-looking moorit rams I have ever seen. That ram graced the paddocks of the Institute until 1933, when I learned that the Inverewe flock of moorit Shetland ewes had no tup. He had served his day in Edinburgh and now went to Inverewe, where he got 55 lambs from the 50 ewes of the flock.

Here were we now with twenty ewes and a tup lamb, all of which carried the blood of that grand tup which came from Unst. I had my pick of five tup lambs at Inverewe and had chosen this one especially for his likeness to the old one I had known so well. It was indeed a proud day for me.

A northerly wind blew up as we went the eight miles to Eilean a' Chleirich, and I was rather anxious for the sheep, which were being thrown about the launch. We had to go slow perforce, though we knew it would be all we could do to put the sheep ashore on the Clerach and get back to Tanera before dark. Patience in a boat is a very great virtue.

I was thankful when we drew alongside the pier rock on the west side of the Clerach. The sheep went ashore a good deal easier than much of the stuff we had hauled up that rock in previous years. When the last had scrambled up the barnacled surface Bobbie jumped ashore herself and drove the sheep through the neck in the rocks to where they could reach the green of the island. The twenty ewes went through there, no worse for their journey, and carrying that eager, questing expression of the beast on new ground. Also they were hungry and the island was lush with a summer's growth. We left them feeding and moving over their new territory. Only the tup lamb was left in the launch, a disconsolate, unsure little figure, not long weaned from his mother and now bereft of all companionship. I was sorry for him, but he had to endure loneliness until 17th November, when the day was calm and we decided to take him out to the Clerach to run with the ewes for six weeks.

As we were about to start we saw Murdo Macleod and the little boat which brings our weekly mail pulling into the Anchorage. There were four figures in the boat, two more than there should be normally. Not until they were in the slip and we had got a glass on them did we see it was Archie Leggate and his wife. They had but a few days of a honeymoon, yet they did us this honour of coming all the way to spend a day with us. Now we were glad indeed the day was in it for taking the tup lamb to Eilean a' Chleirich, for there was nothing these two friends would have loved more than a run out to that island which both knew and associated with earlier happy times. Archie was now a Surgeon-Lieutenant, R.N.V.R., and keen as mustard on the work. All the doubts and arguments of the summer were resolved for him now: war was here, he had found his place in it and he was light of heart.

A calm day between Tanera and the mainland may not mean an easy landing on Eilean a' Chleirich. The very calmness of a frosty day with snow-covered hills and a clear sky may mean a big swell in the Minch. So it was today. All the coasts of the Clerach were ringed in surf as we nosed round trying to find a quiet spot to put the tup ashore. We had fortunately brought the dinghy, a roomy 14-foot Orkney "flattie" we had bought in the previous summer. Bobbie, Margaret and Joan Leggate stayed offshore with the launch while Archie and I went in to the west landing of the island, near the pier rock, which was now quite impossible in this surf. It was fortunately high tide, so that we could row into the inlet with the great boulders with which it is strewn well below us in the water.

Archie was at the oars and brought us in slowly, stern first. But we could not go ashore without bursting a plank or two, or capsizing. I was in the stern with the tup waiting for a slack which comes with rhythmic regularity between the bouts of heavy surf. Archie pushed the boat in a little farther and I picked up the little tup, now christened Ronan, and lowered him into the water, which reached his neck. My heart went out to him in that moment, but in the next I was proud of him. He strode boldly forward, stumbling a little among the rocks, climbed out of the sea, shook himself and purposefully strode up the shingle towards the green. Once there he turned about and looked at us as if to say "I'm all right now". Soon he was gone from our sight into the island, to find his ewes and enjoy a new freedom.

We turned the nose of the launch northwards, rounding the north-west corner of the Clerach and coming into that area of heaving sea which we call the Cauldron. What a heave there was on it now, but no break! The movement of the boat was wild and full of fun, and we laughed in the joy of it all. When we reached the east side of that solitary little island of Glas Leac Beag the flock of three hundred barnacle geese rose from its green surface and hovered above us, now low, now rising, and wheeling away westwards, their undersides glinting white in the low sun. Our homeward path lay north of Tanera Beag and through the islands where the winter birds bobbed in front of us on the water or rose from the band between the tides. There were tysties in their light winter dresses of marbled grey, guillemots with white cheeks and black monocle ribbon, and razorbills and puffins with beaks now unornamented. Purple sandpipers fluttered in the seaweed and bunched together as if in the pleasure of close companionship. It was a perfect winter's day.

That evening at the darkening we took Archie and Joan back to the mainland, putting them ashore on the rocks below Achiltibuie. It was no easy parting for us. His body is now gone, but his personality has remained in no uncertain way, always softening that in us which is hard, inspiring us in the little unselfish things of life and showing his approval of good. I have lost two or three close friends in my life of almost forty years and the sense of loss has remained. Things I do, and ideas I think, cannot be shared with their active minds as such parts of life would have been had they lived, but I do not feel like this about Archie. His personality, or the influence of it, pervades this place where he played and talked as it pervades our minds.

I remember how hard we worked on the quay the following day, as if to make up for what had been in the nature of a pleasure outing, whatever its practical necessity. We came home very tired and the heavy rain in the night caused us to sleep-in on the Sunday morning, 19th November. Thus it was after ten o'clock when I ran down the brae with the crock to milk the little black cow on Ard-na-goine. It is a habit of mine to run on such little errands, not always for the time it saves but because I feel like it. Movement on my feet nearly always gives me physical pleasure. Perhaps this joy in mobility is linked with the fact that I usually find it difficult to fall down; I may stumble, but seem to finish on my feet several yards ahead and a second or two later.

But it was different this Sunday morning. I was wearing a pair of lace-up rubber boots and the rain had made the dying grass of the steep brae very slippy. I was down—thump— almost before I knew I had slipped, and a sharp crack told me a bone had gone. Then came a few moments of intense pain in which my mind saw all the trouble which a broken leg would mean in our circumstances. These disordered seconds passed and I took in a few deep breaths of air which seemed greatly needed.

Here was I with that fracture of the leg associated with the eighteenth-century surgeon, Sir Percival Pott. The fibula snaps on the outside of the leg near the ankle and is in danger of sticking through the skin, as that bone comes near the surface; a process of the tibia, or main leg bone, which projects into the ankle joint, also breaks off, and it is this second and less obvious break which may cause permanent lameness. Pott's dictum, given in the dramatic circumstances of his own accident in a London street, was that the patient must not move or be moved until practised aid is available. He himself had to fight off would-be helpers until a door could be taken off its hinges upon which he could be carried to his hospital.

I had to decide whether to stay there until someone came to look for me—which might be a long time, and what could two women do anyway in carrying the dead weight of a heavy man?—or to get moving somehow. It did not take me long to decide to make for home, because I felt the sooner the leg was freed of boot and sock and into splints before it swelled up, the better it would be for me. So I rolled over on to hands and my right knee with the broken leg stretched out behind me and began the two-hundred-yard journey. It was nothing like so bad as might be imagined. Quite the worst part of the affair was the sight of first Margaret Leigh's face, for she met me a few yards from the house, and then Bobbie's. They were so rudely surprised seeing me come home like a lame sheep.

Once indoors and in the study, Bobbie removed the boot and cut away the sock while I lay on the hearthrug with the leg flexed at the knee. I read her the instructions from a little St. John's Ambulance book while she straightened the limb and got it splinted and bandaged. Then she brought down a little bed to the study and got a fire going for me, and within ten minutes I was in bed with a hot-water bottle on my belly, but chattering my teeth with cold.

Bobbie can always be depended on to be efficient on such occasions. She did not sit looking at me with a long face and asking what we were going to do: she got me a cup of tea in no time and carried on making the steamed pudding at which she was busy when I came creeping in. Margaret Leigh has since said that her most vivid memory of that day was Bobbie's production of a hot dinner (complete with steamed pudding) dead on time, and the fact that we all ate well and heartily. That is as it should be.

The next few hours were unpleasant, for in addition to the pain I suffered from a type of sciatica to which I am prone, in which one or other leg jumps violently every fifteen seconds or so. And this day, of course, it was the broken leg which jumped.

I learned a good deal about myself in the week after this accident. First, I imagined I should have to feed lightly lest I should grow fat lying in bed. Not at all, my appetite was enormous and I rapidly grew thin. I slept about eighteen hours of the twenty-four and read Volume IV of Toynbee's *Study of History* during the wakeful time I was not eating. Within three weeks my hair was greying, though when I recovered every grey hair disappeared. Margaret Leigh having gone home, Bobbie was having a heavy time, not only attending to me but rowing to the mainland in the chancy south-easterly weather we were getting. By her efforts and the promptitude of dear friends in Manchester, we had plaster bandages within ten days. Bobbie soaked them and lagged my leg with them, and I shall not easily forget the immediate comfort which came from the support they provided.

I woke up after the first week, reached for pencil and manuscript book and began writing *Island Years*, a book I ought to have finished before then.

This was a new experience for me, lying around day after day, and I was much interested to note the effect on my output of writing. Normally, when up and about with lots of odd jobs to do, or with my work of watching animals to keep me busy, I find it quite difficult to write a thousand words a day of a book or essay. Now, my meals were carried in to me, and however much I might regret Bobbie having to do everything, the responsibility was lifted from my shoulders, so that I was able to concentrate fully on the job of getting the book written. I found myself able to touch the previously unimagined total of about five thousand words a day. Once I did over six thousand. Such work tired me and I slept like a top all night. It was curious how little my leg bothered me while I remained laid down; as soon as I got upright an awful drawing pain set in in the ankle and I was soon too weak to stay upright.

I shall never forget my first move out of doors on a pair of crutches exactly a fortnight after the accident. The air was delicious, every breath of it sweetness after a fortnight of peat smoke. It was a calm, kindly winter's day and I moved determinedly, though somewhat surreptitiously, across the heather westwards, for there, two hundred yards away, was the crest of the brow, from which unfolded that magnificent view of the Summer Isles in the foreground, then the Minch, and in the far distance the dim Hebrides.

This little journey was a queer mixture of joy and sorrow. There was a child-like gladness in being up for a little while and in achieving the physical task of getting over the rough heather to see that resting panorama, but there was the dreadful feeling that I should never be the active, light-footed person I had been until now. That feeling remained with me for nearly a year, but then the lameness suddenly vanished and all ill effects seemed to go also, and now, in early 1943, I have to think before I can say it was my left leg. Every bit of suppleness has come back and only a slightly enlarged ankle remains to tell the tale.

All the same, this relatively slight accident has had an immense influence on the course of my life. Bobbie and I were in a waiting stage when it happened, working on the quay because it was a job which needed doing, but hesitating whether to turn our energies and few pounds into developing the farm itself. It seemed improbable that we should stay on Tanera for long.

And within a fortnight of my accident the Russo-Finnish War broke and resolved all my doubts about the rights and wrongs of wars and their causation. I burned to go to Finland and cursed my helplessness. Once more the Chamberlain Government appeared to be slow-timing (though for once they were right). The sense of frustration worked in me throughout the winter until that war ended and Germany had entered Scandinavia. By then I had grown accustomed to lameness and, knowing my physical limitations, had finally made up my mind to stay where I was, to put everything that was in me into making this farm from scratch, to demonstrate that in which I had faith—that this wild and neglected country could grow things as well or better than elsewhere if one could but lay aside tradition and think out an husbandry afresh, and that this was worth doing now. War is not the time to drop all that is creative, because man needs a field for creation to toughen the essential quality of hope, and to give reality to the faith which is beyond hope and which says, "This shall be because it is good". I could produce more food for my labour elsewhere, but in starting from scratch on Tanera I was going to work on faith in a principle, and its influence could go beyond the few acres of this island.

But for a broken leg, then, got when doing such a simple homely task as going to milk the cow, there would have been no Island Farm.

Chapter 11

FIRST WINTER

LESS than five weeks after the broken leg I made my first journey in the launch to fetch Alasdair from the mainland on his way home from school for the Christmas holidays. How able a man becomes in accommodating his movements to the dictates of a useless limb! It was the half-mile journey down the cliff path to Tigh an Quay and back again which was troublesome, for there is not room or evenness enough on that track to put the foot of two crutches down at once.

We also picked up a quantity of black-currant and gooseberry bushes and some small apple trees which had been ordered in the early autumn. Slowly, slowly, I made the holes for all these and Bobbie and I planted them. The appearance of these tiny bushes in their orderly rows in that bare garden gave us a thrill of pleasure, but what innocent babes we were! Rona, Clerach and the Treshnish Isles—all wilder than Tanera—had given us quite a false impression of the island which was now our home. Perhaps it was the safety and shelter of the Anchorage which made us think the land itself was more sheltered than it was.

Our lessons have been hard ones since then. All the soft fruit bushes have had to be moved to another piece of ground. The apple trees were put on a sunny slope near the sea, a slope which dipped to the south-east. We have seen those trees grow smaller each year till little is left but the central stock. The winters of 1939-40, 1940-41 and 1941-42 were unusual for the amount of strong east wind, and it is east wind which is the killer. Summer and autumn gales from the south-west prune things, but they do not kill. Our very lives on this island for the first three years seemed to be a battle of a personal nature against east wind. A hedge of Lawson's cypress was planted up the middle of the garden in the autumn of 1940 and was dead by spring, after which we planted up with beech and hawthorn in the spring of 1941. Three days later there

128

XVI*a*. THE QUAY AS THE AUTHOR TOOK IT OVER

XVI*b*. THE QUAY PARTLY RESTORED, JUNE 1940

XVII. THE QUAY FINISHED

came such a storm as we shall never forget and which I shall have cause to mention again. The little thorn buds which had been peeping green were killed and the new hedge made no growth at all that year. Nearly all the beeches succumbed to that storm. That we live and learn is one of my favourite platitudes: we have learnt, and feel the more confident for that learning. The beech and thorn hedge is growing at last, having been mulched and limed each year and watched with eyes of love.

We bought shrubs of various kinds and fifty poplars in the early spring of 1940. All those shrubs are dead now because we did not understand what we were up against. You don't plant something and expect it to grow in this place; you imagine the site in every wind and go and stand there in every wind till you know something of what the plant will feel like. Then you create shelter with stones and treat the little bush more like a calf than as a plant. The poplars were put on the west side of the garden, continuing the line of the old apple trees. The dry-stone dyke gave them shelter from the west and they did not get the worst of the east wind. They have thriven, and now, three years later, some of them are seven feet high and providing perches for singing thrushes. Poplars and soft fruit bushes, now close together, provide a leafiness this place has not known for many a year.

Island Years was finished on Christmas Eve, 1939, after which our household gave itself up to the delights of Christmas for two or three days. All our friends seemed to imagine we were starving on Tanera, so the house was loaded with food which had come as Christmas presents. War had hardly touched the shops and people's private larders at that time. My mouth-organ came out once more to give us the beautiful, simple tunes of carols, while Bobbie and Alasdair sang together with a young friend far from home who was spending Christmas with us.

I still found it more than I could do to stay up and dressed all day, but I was determined to start the new year well by going to Eilean a' Chleirich, gathering our tup lamb from the ewes and doing one or two other oddments. New Year's Day was magnificent, flat calm, sunny, and giving every confidence that it would remain a good day. We were away as soon as it was bright, after picking up a couple of fellows from the mainland who were themselves anxious to catch two sheep which had been left on the Clerach since the previous year.

This was the first of several journeys to the island on which I had to accept the humiliating fact that I was useless on my feet and could only manage the boat. Indeed, I crawled out of the launch on to the pier rock like an old, old man and did nothing all day but potter about the hut and look twice where I put down my feet and my sticks. How scared I was of falling down! That was one of the things the accident afflicted me with for well over a year, a fear of falling down and a tendency to jump almost out of my skin at any sudden noise or unlooked-for appearance of someone past a window or through a door.

The other fellows gathered all the sheep which were on the Clerach, one going across the island and then working the southern ridge towards the west, another going northwards and bringing sheep south-westwards. The man outlined on the ridge could see most of the movements of sheep and man and dog in the northern half and could co-ordinate his work so that the two knots of sheep converged in the little flat of green grass in front of our hut. The Cheviot hoggs which belonged to the crofters were in a white-faced bunch, very nervous, unsure and ready to run wildly anywhere. Our own brown Shetlanders stood close together, also nervous, but not unsure. One or two of the ewes were sizing up the situation with studied care and it was for us to watch those particular animals with especial vigilance. If they broke we should probably lose the lot.

They stood there with their heads high, nostrils on the work, ears going far forward, one foot raised and stamping occasionally. Shetland sheep have not had the brains bred out of them: look at the width of their forehead and between the ears; look at them sideways and see how the face is dished, the nose being relatively small and the brain-pan bulging outwards. How different is a Cheviot's face, which is Roman-nosed, small in the forehead and so narrow between the ears that their tips seem almost to touch, like those of a fancy dog.

plumber who had recently turned a mansion inside out—in a plumber's sense. He had a beautifully finished porcelain sink which was long, deep and narrow, such as might have been made specially for our kitchen. And he was so honest as to say I could have it for fourteen shillings because it was a size nobody wanted—you couldn't put a very wide wash-bowl in it. I also bought a screw flange and three feet of waste pipe from him.

The plumbing system of our new house was most simple. This was our first house in the Highlands which would have a sink at all. Bobbie says she does not mind carrying water in, but she does object to having to take every drop out. I made a strong cradle, reinforced with shelves, to take the heavy sink; I cut a neat little hole in the floor for the waste pipe; then I went outside and dug a hole in the Planestones which was anything but neat. The terrace had originally been built up with rubble, so by getting down four feet into that, good drainage was assured and the broken surface of the rubble would prevent an impervious skin of soap waste forming in the hole. There was a good air space between the bottom of the waste pipe and the hole. All this is contrary to the books and bye-laws, I believe, but it has worked perfectly for three years with never an unpleasant smell. When war catches you without a good roof, it is no good arguing about refinements of plumbing.

But we did make this resolve, not to come down into this little house until it was absolutely ready. It nearly always happens that one is moving gear into a house before the painting and odd work is complete. We went ahead steadily, finishing beadings and facings, painting the whole of the inside of the house except the floor with an undercoating and then pale cream marine paint. There were numerous shelves to make and paint, and in the tiny kitchen I built in a narrow table level with the sink, fitted a chest of drawers on the other side and built a tier of shelves above them. A space was left for the stove, an iron Hestia oven heated by a Primus which we had used with such success on Rona. Two sheets of corrugated iron were nailed to the wooden partition behind the oven as a precautionary measure. And I made an airing rack just above the height of our heads over the oven. Bobbie and I congratulated each other on what we had managed to pack into a kitchen 10 feet by 6 feet.

The living-room was 10 feet by 10 feet and would have to hold best part of a thousand books. This was my one regret, that many of my books would never see the light. The two doors of the living-room were nine inches from the back wall, just wide enough for built-in book-shelves. A wireless set and its impedimenta are a nuisance in a small room, and much as we grudge the space, we had to give ours a little table to itself.

Moving down to the Planestones was a slow business because the gear had to come down the cliff path and my leg would as yet allow of no acrobatics. But at last it was done, the smell of paint had gone, windows were cleaned, the carpet was laid, there were books in position on the shelves and it looked like home. William Daniell's print of the quay and Anchorage was hung above the book-shelves on the back wall of the living-room, facing the scene it portrayed.

It was 20th February, a day we were due to go to Eilean a' Chleirich with the crofters to gather the hoggs and ferry them back to the mainland. What a blessing then, at the end of that long day, to come ashore and for the first time step into the little house at the head of the quay instead of having to stumble up the cliff path! We were too excited to sleep well that night. Next day as we sat at table we looked forth at a view which has never palled: the parapet to the Planestones appears just above the bottom of the window, the quay stretches away obliquely, then the two-mile band of sea, the patchwork quilt of the Achiltibuie crofts, the moor; and beyond this the three isolated groups of mountains, Quinag, Suilven and Canisp, Stac Polly and Cul Mor. It is a mountain view for the epicure, no tumble of mountain after mountain; just these three groups whose shapes are so beautiful that none can excel them in the length and breadth of Scotland.

We see that view every day: we see it as a whole and in all its parts, in every change of weather and season. Now in February the moor is dark and the crofts are drab, and the mountains rise above them a remote and distant country, dark blue with all their features etched sharp with clinging snow. Only rarely do these precipitous hills and terraces take on a totally white face, when a driving blizzard has blown the snow at them horizontally for several hours.

Then in spring and early summer with a north-westerly breeze we see the richest colours: the moor is green then and the sea in front very blue. The crofts have awakened into life with patches of newly growing corn, of brown turnip ground and of dark green potatoes. The mountains become Highland blue, a deep ineffable shade. Blue sky and white clouds are behind them and the sun plays and dapples. Curiously, often we see An Stac dark in shade and Cul Mor behind in sun so that the fantastic shape of this mountain is even more sharply outlined; or the mass Cul Mor may be dark, with the battlements, screes and corries of An Stac shown in the detail of sunlight.

The summer months of July, August and September are unpredictable in the Highlands. They may give good weather or bad, but if the day is to be good we see the mists of the morning wrapping the feet of Quinag, Suilven and Canisp, and as the sun mounts the sky the mists rise to the tops and disappear. And on rainy days at this time you may see the clouds beginning to flocculate round Suilven, and that is a sign that it will soon become fine and turn out a bright evening.

North wind and snow squalls in winter will take away all the view except that of the moor and the mainland shore. Beyond is a dull dark curtain of grey in which the snow is lashing the mountain country. Then the squall is gone and the sun shines through an atmosphere vividly clear to show the mountains in sun and shadow all the way to Ben Stac and the Fionaven group, beyond which there are no more mountains in Scotland.

Few ships or small boats come into the Anchorage of Tanera now, but for us sitting at our window there is equal interest in the constant traffic of birds, the character of which changes with the season. In the few February days left after moving down to the little house on the Planestones we would see the great northern diver, two or three of them, sailing majestically about the Anchorage; sometimes diving quietly and rising again with a fish, sometimes becoming half playful and diving with a little white splash which partook of the nature of display.

We hear their weird call sometimes and think of the bird then as the loon, the name by which it is known in Canada. Later in the spring the laughing cry becomes more strongly developed, and before the birds finally leave us in June I have seen a full-length session of display between a pair of birds. What a wonderful sight it is to see the great birds standing in the water, wings stretched wide and the head working sinuously! The great northern diver does not breed nearer than Iceland, but it is to be seen in the Anchorage as early as 10th September in some years and as late as 12th July.

Those close relatives of the divers, the grebes, are common winter visitors to the Anchorage. Even as I write I can see a band of five Slavonian grebes three hundred yards beyond the quay. They are active, strong birds, much given to beginnings of display which strike the watcher as being in the nature of conversation within the group. And every day one or two pairs of little grebes come fishing in the shallows. Sometimes you can lean over the parapet of the quay and watch the little grebes immediately below, swimming on the water with their heads under or diving with a little chuck of their bodies almost clear of the water and working the shingle for very tiny crabs and marine worms. Black-necked and red-necked grebes are seen occasionally in winter, and the crested grebe each spring on migration.

A pair of greater black-backed gulls and a pair of herring gulls haunt the Anchorage all winter, either floating quietly on its surface or flying above, but rarely standing on the shore. When summer comes, these gulls are still there, now spending much time walking about the seaweed at low tide or standing on the parapet of the quay. Is it a greater profusion of water-edge life in summer which accounts for this differing behaviour?

Common gulls nest on the larger island in the Anchorage and become more numerous during February, until the whole flock is roosting near the water-edge by the middle of March. They bring a new sound to the Anchorage, heralding the tardy spring, and throughout the summer they tamely work the seaweed in the harbour or join the hens at feeding-time if they are given a chance.

The heron is there day and night through the winter, stalking the shallows and finding eels in our harbour, for a freshwater drain runs into it and attracts these fish. The movements and long spells of immobility of our herons seem a constant delight to our guests, and indeed their slow flight, their landings and takings-off, their postures and lightning beak thrusts, are spectacular. These birds have bred on the shores of the Anchorage in the past and began nesting on our cliff in February 1941, but the wretched east wind blew all their sticks away and caused them to lose heart.

The summer scene in the Anchorage is much changed. There is more liveliness to watch as we sit taking our food. A colony of Arctic terns which nest on the little island is now in a fever of activity, using our parapet as a social centre and hovering and dapping for little fish in the harbour. If the launch is anchored off the quay a number of them perch on that and chatter continuously. Courting eider ducks and drakes are there in May and June, and resplendent mergansers, and by the end of that month both of these ducks are appearing in and about our harbour and in the Anchorage with broods; the eiders never have more than five and usually only three or four, but the mergansers appear with a dozen to fourteen ducklings. What mites of energy the little mergansers are! They can swim at a great speed for such little things, and if they wish to hurry they raise themselves on the water and hydroplane along its surface at as fast a pace as a man could run.

From about the middle of July the young common gulls are swimming about, calling in that unmusical voice which is like an unoiled door-hinge, always calling to their parents for more food. The young terns seem much more independent at this time, and perhaps they really are, for in a few weeks they will be making a journey on their own of several thousand miles to the Southern hemisphere.

All this we watch from our window and it is a pageant of which we never tire. The night-time, also, in the little house on the Planestones was something of a new experience for us, for it is nearer the shore than any of the tents or huts in which we have lived on the other islands. When the weather is calm we hear the plash of the sea just a few yards from our heads, a constant accompaniment to the calls of the birds of the night.

There are curlews on the beach and on Fank Point, sometimes the note of a purple sandpiper comes through the window to us of a winter's night, and often that of a ringed plover. I have never seen a ringed plover on our beach in day-time, though they come at night. This is strange behaviour for such a tame bird of the shingle.

To come down to that little wooden place on our own ground was in the nature of a fulfilment. We were happy and hopeful of the future. We not only owned a bit of derelict ground but were occupying it, and felt a tremendous surge of energy rising within us to make that ground fruitful.

As yet the gaps in the dykes were not built up and our neighbour's cattle and sheep wandered round our very doors and over all the land except the acre of garden. It was difficult getting this work done, and when it was finished there was nothing in the nature of production to be seen for the immense labour. What a sense of privacy we got from having a gate at either end of the Planestones! And when we saw our ground completely free of Cheviot sheep for a whole day we felt we could see about getting cattle of our own on the place.

Chapter 12

THE UNFORGETTABLE YEAR

NO one can divorce his own affairs and doings from the international events of 1940, however remote in body he may have been from them. I put it down as one of the queerest years of my life, one of mental confusion clouding the perfect physical conditions in which I seemed to be living. In March I was active enough to go down to Berwick-on-Tweed in my old Ford, to finish off the investigation I had begun before the war on the influence of the grey seals on the salmon-fishery of the Tweed Estuary. There was little hint of war then on that part of the East Coast; this peering, keeking biologist nosing about the coast and crossing the wet sands in his car to Holy Island was never once accosted or looked on as a spy. There was good food in the hotel and I received delightful hospitality from friends in the town. Only the black-out was strange and unbeautiful, and on one journey up the coast in the Tweed Commissioners' motor coble I saw a red gash in the cliff which was the spot where a mine had washed ashore and exploded. Six months later, all this would have been impossible to do.

Few people can have experienced the war as we have so far. Physically, we are remote from it, though in some ways we are nearer it intellectually. This journey to Berwick was the first I had seen of war-time Britain; it was like making a visit from Mars; little things like anti-blast preparations on shop windows and various black-out gadgets impressed me though they had become everyday affairs to other people. Then back to remote-ness again, where we *heard* all about the war in the wireless news and commentaries. Serving soldiers, I have since come to understand, are not in such close contact with war intellectually. They do their own jobs and do not listen to the news, read the papers or study the whole military and naval situations. We do, and find ourselves much more serious about the whole business than those more actively engaged. Still later in the year and during the following winter of heavy air-raids, the attitude of outsiders who came to see us was definitely optimistic and cheerful, but in the remote Highland townships there was a deep gloom not wholly to be accounted for by the fate of the 51st Division in June.

To all intents and purposes, the war began for us with the invasion of Norway. The news altered its tone and spoke no more of the ripe-plum qualities of Saarbrücken. Yet it remained unduly elated. Even Mr. Churchill thought Hitler had made a vast mistake in going to Norway, and the epic battles, in which such severe naval losses were inflicted on the enemy, did make things look brighter. But we on Tanera got our weekly newspaper a week or a fortnight after it was published, and as the news at that time was progressively getting worse, to read week- or fortnight-old news was doubly depressing. Newspapers are not meant to be read several days after their issue. The special correspondents and the commentators stated their reasons for being practically certain that the Germans could not do something or other and that we should be able to make a determined stand at such and such a place. But by the time we read these papers the Germans had done the almost impossible and we had already come to understand how we were unable to hold our position. No, on an ebbing tide of fortune old newspapers should be eschewed, as a very necessary discipline.

The Norwegian news was bad enough in this early and delightful spring, in which we had worked as hard as our bodies would take us and were as happy in our immediate surroundings as we could hope to be. Three tons of basic slag and two tons of ground limestone had come to Badentarbet Pier, and this we had to ferry over, some by launch but most of it in the dinghy because it saved petrol. Slag is very heavy stuff, packed in 1¼-cwt. bags, and I found it hard on my mending leg to get the bags out of the boat on to the quay and each bag from the ground to the best position for carrying, on the top of my shoulders. Fifteen hundredweight of this high-grade slag and half a ton of the limestone went into the acre of garden, and that was easy—a short journey from the quay and no hills to climb. But the remaining three and three-quarter tons were

the top of Nettlebed Piece in the garden was properly dug, manured and limed for them. A wall was to the east and another at the back of them to the north—the gable end of the tiny house by the shore where the old bachelor with second sight had lived. Those sweet peas began to flower on 13th June and thereafter gave us hundreds of blooms. There they were, a tiny world of fragrance and peace while France was falling and our ideas getting the biggest jolt they had ever had.

My mother came to visit us in the first week of May in that year and, as might be imagined, there had been a good redding-up in preparation. I was the happiest of men next day when Bobbie and I took her round with us in the launch to the coral sand beach of Tanera Beag. My mother sat there on the white sand enjoying what is one of the quietest scenes among the islands while Bobbie and I filled sacks and waded out with them to the boat. But the next morning Holland and Belgium were invaded. Instead of having quietness, my mother was to grow increasingly unsettled. When danger threatens, one wishes passionately to get home to one's own place. Our island conditions had not the grace of my mother's home, but it was not the roughness and inconvenience which were troubling her; it was the passionate desire for her own corner, which must be understood and given sympathy in ageing folk.

The weather was the most perfect we have ever had here— and the news grew worse each day. My mother loves her meals out of doors and we had every meal outside for three weeks on end. We would have breakfast on the Planestones, near the parapet and overlooking the sea. Lunch would be in the shade of the south wall of the walled garden-to-be, and at tea-time we would carry the table through into the garden and set it in the domed bower made by the old apple trees. They were in blossom then and humming with bees throughout the day. It seemed all wrong to have this perfection in that time of horror. The blow which fell on the whole West Highland area at that time was a crushing one. Many thousands of the Highland Division, the 51st, were taken prisoner and many good men of the district were killed. Of thirteen men in the 4th Seaforths from Achiltibuie alone, eleven were taken prisoner. One man, Donnie (Beag) Macleod who has passed

through the pages of *Island Years*, had the good fortune to be
wounded at Abbeville and escape the prison camp by exercising
his stalking abilities. He returned to Britain on that famous
"last boat from Bordeaux". The wound was not serious,
Donnie was awarded the D.C.M., and now that gay singer
of Gaelic songs has fought with the Desert Army in its proud
campaign from El Alamein to Tunis.

Bobbie and my mother and I were round to Tanera Beag
again for coral sand at the next low spring tide. This beautiful
stuff is pure calcium carbonate and has fertilized hundreds of
acres of this countryside. It is necessary to apply it heavily, at
the rate of about ten tons to the acre of black ground, but when
this is done, the ground will need no more lime for twenty
years. I seem to be the only man using it at the present time,
though there is not an acre in Coigach but what would do with
a good dressing. When I applied a mere two tons of ground
limestone to a bit of our ground in that spring of 1940 it was
because I wanted the quick results it could give, until I could
back it up with some loads of coral sand.

On this day the weather seemed perfect and we loaded up
with over two tons. The labour was heavy for a man and
a woman, so we left the last five hundredweight in the dinghy
which we had in tow.

But I did not trim that five hundredweight as carefully as
I might have done. This was an example of carelessness when
one is tired, which is the cause of many avoidable accidents.
It would not have mattered at all had the weather stayed as it
was, and had we been coming from Eilean a' Chleirich we
should certainly not have been careless, but here we were in
narrow waters never more than a few yards from shore and
we did not think.

Then a south-easterly breeze sprang up as we made for the
north point of Tanera and was quite strong as we turned south
into the sound. I began to be a little concerned for my mother,
who does not like the sea and is the one person easier made
seasick than myself.

I need not have bothered.

As we passed Iolla Chapuill, a rock in the sound north-east
of Tanera, we had to go farther out from shore, and off that

rock the waves are often steep because of the shelving of the sea-floor. Two such steep waves hit us plumb and the heavily laden launch took a lot of water. That did not matter much, but the dinghy in tow could not rise so easily; the waves also caught her and filled her. I put the gear in neutral to stop the boat, but I dared not stop the engine just off that rock with this wind. My mother took the tiller quite calmly and kept the boat's head to the sea while Bobbie and I were reaching over the stern for our dinghy. She suddenly sank and held for a moment or two by the painter, but the still slowly moving propeller cut the painter like a knife and our dinghy disappeared. Those five hundredweights of sand had slipped down under the thwarts to make so firm a ballast that there was no hope of the dinghy emptying and rising to the surface again. Bobbie and I were numbed with this serious loss. Where would we get another dinghy in these days?

We said nothing, but took the tiller from my mother and came on home. The complete incident could be written off as about 25 per cent. bad luck and about 75 per cent. carelessness and bad management. Next day and the day after we were out with a glass-bottomed box in a flat calm sound, searching the dim sea-bottom for a gleam of white which might be the dinghy. The salmon-fishing crew from Badentarbet also helped by bringing a coble, between which and the launch we hung a drag chain on long warps and made repeated circuits of the whole area where the dinghy sank.

But we caught nothing but weed.

One man made me smile with his unconscious disregard for any help a woman might be in a boat. As the West Highlander does, he was trying to excuse me for what he knew quite well was a piece of carelessness.

"Och, how else would it be now, and you alone in the boat?"

The loss of that dinghy cast a gloom over the next week or two. She was only a year old, a cheap white-pine flattie such as the Orkney yards turned out for less than £1 a foot before the war. She was 13 feet 6 inches long and 5 feet 6 inches in the beam, very light to haul and extraordinarily easy to row. You could tread about in her and she would remain steady, and even if I stood on the gunwale where she was widest there would still be two or three inches of freeboard. She was particularly useful for carrying sheep, holding up to a dozen comfortably, and so steady when they tended to pack to one side or the other.

I telegraphed to Orkney to see if another boat could be got, but no. There is only one yard building small boats on the north-west Highland coast, and their tradition is one of strength and weight rather than lightness. The once prosperous Gairloch boat-building industry has now quite gone. We were lucky to get a 13-foot dinghy by steamer from Colquhouns' of Dunoon for £14. This little boat is 5 feet in the beam and seems very much smaller than our flattie. I would not like to move sheep about in her, for it would be sheer cruelty to the boat.

Having completed the fencing of the big park to the state of being cattle proof, we got our first cow. She was a rather ugly black beast belonging to our old friend Mrs. Fraser, Raon Mor. The cow had certain qualities which I knew : first, she had the virtue of youth, being less than four years old ; she was a persistent milker, which is worth a lot under our conditions, and she was exceptionally good as a butter cow. This does not mean that she gave milk as rich as a Jersey's—it contains probably not more than 4·25 per cent. of butter fat—but her milk has the idiosyncrasy of containing large fat globules. Thus, the cream rises quickly and almost completely and can be skimmed off in one thick blanket. When you have just two or three cows of your own and milk is an important item of diet you learn that milk is not just milk, but a fluid of varied qualities depending on the individuality of the cow, the period of the lactation and the time of year.

This black cow, which we called Bluebell because she came here when the wild hyacinths had begun to bloom, yields the milk which we like to set for butter. Not only does the cream rise so completely, but the texture and colour of her butter are very good. We do *not* like her milk for the tea, because the quick rising of the cream means an excellent first cup and the lower half of the milk jug contains a thin, blue skim milk which gives no body to the tea. The next cow we bought gave a milk of small fat globules which did not rise readily and formed no sharply demarcated layer of cream in the setting bowls.

Thus she is not particularly economical as a butter cow, but for tea and all other purposes her milk is preferable.

Milk is sweetest and fullest of flavour when the cows are freshly calved and at grass. A stale cow gives a flavourless milk. All these points are watched by the household living on their own produce. You become most decidedly epicurean when you feed largely on what you grow, and it is a right and sound development. We are meant to enjoy our food, and it is right that the simplicity and innate flavour of fresh home-grown foods should provide that enjoyment rather than the complex spicy kind of cookery necessary to titillate the jaded palate to stale ordinary food. I shall have cause to return to this subject because we found it so important, but given what I have said about the qualities of milk, there still remains technique in drinking it, almost as if it were wine. Milk is at its best as it comes from the cow, having lost none of its natural heat and not having been agitated by straining or overmuch pouring. When I was a lad I knew the taste of the milk of all the cows I milked and had my favourites. As I finished one of these favourites I would lift the bucket, twist round a quarter of a turn on my stool and take a long pull. It was glorious. Milk is both sweet and salty, but the sweetness masks the saltiness when the cow is fresh. If you drink milk at lunch as we do, it should be taken with the savoury course, for once the sweet pudding has passed through your mouth milk tastes thin and flavourless.

Well now, this cow: the worst thing about her was her looks. She was no good advertisement of herself. The only nice thing in her appearance was her eyes, which were soft and violet and highly intelligent. As I have come to know and love her I have come to watch those eyes closely, but I watch them nothing like so closely as they watch me. That cow knows me as well as my mother does.

We brought her over in the launch one calm day, from a rock just north of Badentarbet Pier where, at half tide, the boat could be brought alongside and there was a considerable platform at which we could work. County Council and Department of Agriculture piers are no good to us for moving animals, or indeed anything heavy, in small boats. Such piers are high above a launch even at high spring tide, and they are not usually supplied with a derrick for lowering heavy gear. Cows and sheep, then, are always loaded from traditional convenient rocks which were there long before the piers.

We had covered the floor of the forward part of the launch with turves and we had plenty of old sacks to put over the gunwale as the cow was lifted inboard. Bluebell is in many ways a sensitive, nervous cow, but she is neither foolish nor hysterical. She did not like getting into the launch—what cow would? But no one could have had greater consideration. The Badentarbet salmon-fishing crew came along to help, petting the cow so much and showing her a sheaf of corn in the boat, that between greed and fussing she was lifted bodily into the launch before she fully knew what was happening. There she stood quiet, with Murdo Macleod sitting on the forepeak holding the halter and patting her neck.

It was quite easy going ashore on our own quay, for the end of it was still unfinished and sloped down six feet from its proper level. Bluebell knew the idea was to go ashore and that the chances were there would be more doing ashore than standing here in a strange wobbly thing in which there was the continuous noise of an engine. She stepped out of the boat herself, climbed carefully up the steep ramp of stones to the finished part of the quay and looked around with her ears forward. We took her along to the walled garden where a crop of fresh grass was growing on the limy rubble. Phew! What stuff! she said, and wasted no more time looking about. That would come in an hour's time when her belly was full.

She was pretty thin then, scurfy in the skin and showing every sign that it was the end of the winter. May is the time when the owner of cattle is not overproud of his stock and takes no great delight in showing them to people. The weather is bright then, saying it is summer, but grass is still scarce. The bellies of the cattle are held high through having had dry food, and that food itself is past its best by the end of April, so that the poor things look worse than they are in the brilliant sunshine and greening grass.

There was no grazing in Achiltibuie to equal what we could offer Bluebell this summer. She began to grow all ways and not merely put on flesh. After calving on 10th June she milked better than I expected—up to three and a half gallons a day. But she dropped to two and a half in August, at which time I was spending less time working in the big park, and in addition to the grass lessening in value she was lonely.

A cow is a sociable creature, and if there is no other bovine animal for company she is well satisfied with a human being. To many men cattle are just so much property, to be properly treated because that is the way they pay best, but I look at cattle in a different way. A cow is my favourite beast as a pet, for she has many nicer characteristics than a dog has and much more intelligence than a horse. There is more to it than that also : let me set it down in all seriousness, with Bluebell as the example.

She came to us and had no other beast near her; we petted her and she liked it. There was a lot of dyke-building and fencing with barbed wire to be done in her park and she would come to inspect it all and lie down beside us as we worked. Then she calved and this bull calf was taken away from her before she got any notion of it at all. But I smelt of that calf and it was I who drew the milk from her. Her flood of mother love had to go somewhere and it was spent on me. And yet she knew me as a giver of food and she knew I had power over her. Thus do a man and a cow attain to an almost mystical union and relationship. The man is both child and lord to the animal, and for the man the animal becomes the object before which he lays the fruits of his labours in the fields and from which he draws through his hands the very stream of life.

This cow Bluebell in her loneliness came to rely on me unduly. Wherever I moved about the place she wished to follow, and though she might not see me the wind would carry my scent and her muzzle would go up to assess my position before she would trot over to find me. It was a nuisance altogether, so I looked about for a second cow in self-defence. Bluebell, also, was a gate-crasher. She has been responsible for my making most of the gates about the place, which would otherwise have had to wait till I had more time. Apart from me, food is her other passion. She is the greediest cow I have ever struck, and has an eye for ever cocked on the chance of seeing something to eat. She will look into any unclosed door on the chance of finding something, because experience has led her to remember that many edible things are to be found in places where cows are not supposed to go. Whereas I merely make sure with the other cattle, and know there are some liberties I can take because animals are not quite as smart as men, I must make doubly sure with Bluebell and remember that she is not as absent-minded as I am.

Our ground is heavily infested with ticks; from all I can hear, Tanera always has been noted for its millions of ticks. Bluebell began to collect them about her body before the end of July. These loathsome bloodsuckers hang mainly on the parts where the skin is thinnest—under the throat, between and behind the fore-legs, along the milk vein, in the crease made by the forward part of the udder and the belly, between the quarters of the udder and between it and each hind leg. Larval forms, known as seed ticks, would cling in serried ranks on her eyelids. Bluebell knew she was being irritated, but she also knew that a man could help to stop that irritation. How often has she come and shoved her great behind into me, asking for the ticks to be removed! Each day at milking times I would remove and squash all that were in the region of her udder, but definite de-ticking appointments were necessary as well. When removing them from her belly region it was easiest to lie flat on the ground, where this most clumsy of cows would allow me to lie between her legs without danger of being trodden on. I think the most striking example of her confidence in man's power to relieve her of irritation is her attitude to my removing the tiny ticks on her eyelids: I hold her head in my arm, where she lets the weight of it rest freely, and then pull off the parasites one by one with a pair of fine forceps. The eye is a tender place on man or beast, and few animals will allow their eyes to be touched without remonstrance.

Bluebell is with us still, having now had three calves while in our care. They have all been black bull calves and therefore not worth our keeping, but they have been good ones and have fetched high prices. Each year I say I will get rid of her, because she is so ugly and so naughty, but I love the cow dearly and more than the others, so I dare say she will stay a while longer.

The poor beast would be deeply hurt if I dumped her on someone else, for she feels tied to us and this place far closer than the other cattle do.

All this pleasure in my cow was growing while our Army was being pushed back to the sea in France, while they escaped, and while France dropped ignominiously out of the war. I felt my very personality being torn apart at that time, racked by the desire to get into the fighting and the knowledge that I was no good yet in that propensity. The path of action is the easy one in a crisis.

The sun kept on shining, telling us it was the best of all worlds. We lived in a land of beauty unscarred by war, yet all we held dear was in the direst danger. It was a fantastic world, this of 1940.

We had to think about Alasdair, who was at school near the Moray coast. A way home must be explained and maps given him so that in an emergency he could find his way through the hills. I had confidence in the boy that he could do this in a fortnight. There was a suggestion from his school that he might join a party of children being evacuated to Canada. We had to decide whether or no, both on personal grounds and on the larger issue of the position of children in the country as a whole. Alasdair's home was not on the east or south-east coast of England; he was not living in a tenement or crowded area of London; why should he go away? Because we might be scared? If we said "No, he stays here", were we putting our pride before prudence? Anyway, we decided he should remain here. It was not for children of people in our position to leave Britain.

And since my mother's home was now in the south-east corner of England, I had to think of her too. I was in no position to say yes or no to her, and she, being without fear, said she was going back and would not evacuate her home unless compelled by our own military authorities. It was hard saying goodbye to her, though I was warmed by her tremendous faith. Events justified it.

Alasdair came home in due course for his summer holidays; the Battle of Britain was fought and won; we got our hay in without a shower, and my hard labour of the spring looked as if it would result in a heavy crop of swedes for the cows, of potatoes and vegetables for ourselves, and in growing promise for the year ahead. The news steadied. Some of the feeling of exasperation at what seemed my ineffectuality passed from me; for let it be understood, I in this remoteness could share none of that heroic, elate steadfastness which was borne by the people of industrial Britain and those of the southern and eastern coasts. We were not sharing their immediate danger; we could only admire our fellows from a safety we almost despised.

Chapter 13

MAKING THE FARM

THE rushes in the big park looked a formidable forest of dark green when viewed from the gateway at the west end of the walled garden. They were waist-high, the result of many years' unchecked growth. Rushes increase rapidly in pasture because the grazing animals carefully clip the grass all round the clumps and thus remove all competition. The clumps spread and join until grass almost disappears. One grass does seem to persist in an attenuated form—that awful weed of arable land, onion couch grass. Normally it would disappear from a pasture, for the conditions of close turf do not favour its spread, but it can grow in the heart of a thick clump of rushes, using the fibrous mat as one would plant bulbs in compost. I did not know this until I made a positive attack on the rushes by buying a short, heavy, old-fashioned wrought-iron scythe blade which I fixed to an American snath, and cutting them. When I say cutting them I do not mean running the blade through them an inch or two from the ground. That is not cutting rushes, it is pruning them with a view to getting a stronger growth next year.

I have an idea that only a strongish man in his prime can cut rushes as they should be done with intent to eradicate them, and even then that man would need to be cutting his own rushes rather than someone else's or he would tend to lose heart. It is work which either breaks your back or develops its strength to unimagined endurance. When a man uses a scythe in grass he maintains a steady sweep and the sharpness of his blade and the sweetness of his action takes the scythe through with comparatively little effort in relation to the work done. That is as it should be, but when attacking a high, clumpy crop of rushes the steady sweep gets you nowhere. A hard snatch is necessary, the force of which comes on both arms and back together. The blade must go in level, but deep, so that the crown is taken off the clump entirely and you look

155

down on to a lovely pattern of densely packed circles and ovals of white pith. The rushes do not like such exposure at all: sun and rain beating into their heart sap their strength. But they are not dead, only weakened. If the ground is then heavily grazed by cattle, the young growth of the rushes will be plucked off and the already injured crowns are not helped by heavy feet cutting into their middles. Next year the ground may be cut for hay, which means that the rushes have to compete with the grass on what are now rather less than equal terms. They make a poor show and the presence of a few rush stems among the hay is an advantage rather than a nuisance in a wet climate, for their stiffness keeps the grass springy so that it dries better in the field and can be carried as hay to the barn in a wetter condition than if it was all grass. The rushes prevent heating in the stack.

One more experiment on the extermination of rushes was a successful one: I put a good layer of coral sand over the newly exposed crowns of the rush clumps in one patch of the park. This practice did two jobs at once, liming the soil as well as rush killing. The clumps were reduced to raised places in the sward by the next year, through which the plough cut with ease. I should like to have done this over the whole park, but, as always, the time factor prevents many of the farmer's good intentions becoming fact. A single-handed farmer is always trying to catch up with time.

That rushy ground should be in such condition that it can be ploughed in the following year, assuming that it has been made dry enough by draining. But rushes are as much an indication of sour land as wet. I have seen them spreading fast in relatively dry, well-drained fields which were short of lime.

A good man working twelve hours of the day can cut about an acre of grass, but he would not get more than a quarter of an acre of fifty-year-old rushes cut through the crown. And he would not work twelve hours a day on the job. I would spend five or six hours hacking the rushes and I did about two acres in 1940. Some of the ground is now growing oats—but that is running ahead. The immense bulk of cut rushes dried quickly in that wonderful year of early summer weather and gave us a biggish job carrying them into a stack at the foot of Cnoc an-t-Sidhe. We have no horses here, for the nature of the ground is such that they would be uneconomical to keep; all carrying of light bulky stuff such as rushes, hay or corn is done in a sheet of sacking, Norwegian fashion. In this way I can manage sixteen to twenty sheaves of corn at a load, and as much dry rushes as can be packed into the sheet. It is quite an economical way of transport as long as barn or stack is not too far from the job; otherwise too much time is spent walking back empty. But there is no better way open to us, so whether we like it or not we have to do it.

This stack of rushes gave us excellent bedding for the cows all winter. How happy I was to see them standing belly-deep in their stalls in the sweet-smelling stuff, their coats shining clean and with a feed of hay at their heads! But I am not sure that rushes help to make such good manure as I had intended they should. They do not rot down in the manure heap like straw, and as far as I can see, the manure heap made from rush bedding does not get hot at all. I have used the manure in the rows on which I have grown cabbages and swedes, and when the ground has been dug in the following year the manure has turned up again apparently very little rotted. In 1941 I moved one manure heap and sprinkled sulphate of ammonia over each layer as I rebuilt it. Such treatment should result in heating and rotting of the bedding as the heap was open to the rain, but the rushes were still quite rushlike and stiff when I used the heap in the mangold rows of 1942. Given the rushes, I should still use them for bedding and they are the best possible stuff for covering potato and other root clamps, but the problem has ceased to interest me so much since our farm will produce no more heavy crops of rushes. Had the choice been open to me, I think the best way of turning the rushes into manure would be by putting them into a yard or building in which young cattle were being wintered untied. The constant and even treading would have broken them down mechanically, as well as the chemical effect of the urine on the ever-thickening layer.

A dry store was an absolute necessity to us before we did any other constructional job on the farm. We decided to roof in a building on the northern side of the Planestones, measuring

20 feet by 10 feet, for which we had bought corrugated iron before the war had become serious. Like all such jobs, it meant a lot of getting ready before doing the actual work. The front wall had to be lowered and levelled to a height of eight feet. This bit of wall is unique about this place in the toughness of its mortar. Coral sand does not appear to have been used, only hot lime in a manner which I have been told by natives of the North-West is not known now. It is extremely hard work to part stone from stone, or indeed to get the point of a pick into the junction. The jarring was sufficient to bring blisters even to my hands, which I had thought long past that stage. I made a hole in the back wall for a window—a foolish thing to do as I soon found out, for that wall was mortared only with a poor clay without any lime. I nearly let the whole lot down about my ears.

The wood for this building came from the old house. Now that we were living on the Planestones it had become unsafe to move about near Tigh an Quay. If the weather was wild, slates would fly and dig into the earth when they whizzed down. The quickest way of getting the slates off was to punch the sarking off from below, standing on the uppermost floor of the building and using a pole as a ram. Most of the slates were flaked and rotten round the nail-hole, so they shook off fairly easily before the sarking itself was clear of the rafters. This technique worked splendidly till we neared the ridge of the roof, which called for our standing more to the middle of the floor. A young friend, Edward Booth, was staying with us at the time, helping with the work of the place until he was to join the Navy in the autumn. He was standing in the middle of the floor in the haunted room battering at the sarking with his pole when every floor joist collapsed at once at its junction with the wall. I happened to be on the first joist of the adjacent room when this happened, and saw the whole floor going down like a lift, but rather faster. Edward was going down also, in a sitting posture, but with thin air under his seat. The whole outfit fetched up on the next floor but one with a great crash and an incredible uprising of dust. Edward climbed out a little shaken and with a bruise on his hip where he had managed to strike the edge of a mantelpiece on the way down. That was

the end of the haunted room of Tigh an Quay. A thrush nested
in one of the joist-holes in the wall last year and its mate sang
joyously from the gaunt chimney-stack above.

As the summer wore on I had to think seriously about a byre.
Bluebell had herself chosen the most westerly compartment
of the main range of buildings as the place where she preferred
to stand when being milked. It also seemed the most sensible
place to build the byre if I could get the roofing material, but
before the roofing there was a three-foot layer of soil and rubble
on the floor.

There was nothing for it but steady work.

The August rains had come, and as we dug into that sixteen-
foot square mass we were disagreeably surprised to find the
earthy part of the rubble was clay. Where did it come from?
How did it get into there? There are many mysteries about
this place in the way of accumulation of rubbish. At this time
we did no more than sling the stuff out of the window-hole
and wheel the stones into two heaps in the desolation of the
walled garden. We have done a good deal of clearing before
and since then, but nothing has been so hard. The one bright
spot was when we found there was a floor of red brick underneath all the rubbish.

Once more the old house became Crusoe's ship in providing
wood for the cow-stalls and calf-pen. I had to splice rafters
to make them reach across the building and supported the splice
by running a length of timber vertically from the floor. These
vertical supports to the roof were so arranged that they played
their part in forming the stalls. The corrugated iron for the
roof had not come yet, so I lashed and tacked a roof of canvas
and boards on to the rafters just above the cow-stalls, and if
the truth be told the animals lay there comfortably until 22nd
November, when I fetched the roofing from Badentarbet
Pier and got it fixed the same afternoon. I got a window from
the house and cemented it into the upper half of the window-
hole of the byre, the lower half being walled up and cemented.
Then I brought in a lot of rushes and stacked in the corner.
The byre became then what it has been ever since, a quiet and
delightful place where our guests love to congregate. I would
as soon sit in a byre in which there is plenty of hay or bedding

and where contented animals are eating or chewing the cud
as I would sit in an armchair in the house. Indeed I would
rather do so, for the body can relax utterly laid in the straw
in such quiet company. Milking times are to me times of
sheer pleasure, for the byre and its occupants extend a feeling
of welcome.

Some day soon I shall have to build raised concrete standings
for the cows, but so far I have had no time for the job—nor
any great inclination if the truth be known. Who would have
thought that I, the exponent of clean milk production and
adviser on cow-shed floor construction at the age of twenty-one,
would have descended to this state of a primitive peasant before
he was forty, content to see his cows lying on a level brick
floor, on a great compacting bed of rushes? There are neither
regrets nor remorse; the cows are healthy and comfortable
and they will develop no big knees or calloused hocks from cold
hard concrete!

Let me tell you more of what this man of science is not doing
according to the books, and what his attitude is to the practical
application of science to such a complex of natural history as
agriculture is. I am wholly in favour of anyone engaging in
farming having a scientific education in the principles of agriculture, but that education should not be designed to give him
a set of ineluctable precepts on which, if he keeps them, he
cannot go wrong. A scientific training should bring a man to
know how things work, or if he does not know something new
to his observation, how to find how it works. Training in
science should also so raise a man's powers of observation of
natural phenomena that he gets into the way of finding problems
which need solution. A farmer who knows the biology, the
chemistry and the physics of the processes of tilling soil, culti-
vating crops, breeding animals and feeding them has a large
measure of command, and that command is surer because it
is elastic in operation. He can deviate from recognized practices
in altering circumstances because he knows what is happening
and how far he can deviate without causing a breakdown of
a process.

The man who goes so far towards recognizing the value of
science as to collect the practical results of research and experi-

XVIII. BARNACLE GEESE GRAZING (*see page* 210)

rubbing not only detaches loose particles of bedding, hair and scurf, but pleases the cow and brings down her milk. I milk and strip carefully and weigh the milk (for recording is one of the joys of keeping cows), but when I pour out from the pail into the tin setting pan in the dairy I pour from the side of the bucket which was nearest me because a few hairs and specks collect on the inside of the bucket farthest away. Bobbie scalds each setting bowl every day, but the milking pail rarely gets a scald. The milk is poured from it in less than a minute after it comes from the cow, and immediately I go to the rain-water butt to let the water run all round the inside and outside of the bucket. By never letting it stand, there is never a hint of semi-dried milk adhering to the bucket. Our milk keeps sweet for thirty-six hours and more even in the height of a thundery August. It does not get a chance to keep longer than that. When we were short of milk for a little time in September, 1942, and were unable to make butter and soft cheese, we lost our continuity of souring organisms and had great difficulty when the cows calved again to get the milk to go sour at all. Our souring is a good clean lactic acidity which we should never dream of infecting by bringing into the house an average sample of West Highland crowdy or butter.

We bought our second cow in October, 1940, from a man who was giving up his croft and going to work on munitions in Glasgow. I do not suppose he looked upon the change of occupation as a misfortune, but I was certainly sorry to see him go, for it meant one more croft going to ruin. His cow was a blue-polled one, probably the best in Coigach. She was not only outstanding as a milker but of such shape as would grace the best herds of dual-purpose cattle. She moved with an action equal to that of a Highland cow. The only fault I could see in her was a touch of sullenness in the eye.

The same ritual was followed in ferrying over this cow, but even more care was taken as she was a heavier beast. Alec Mathieson, from whom I bought her, provided a little light relief by backing across the launch with the sheaf of corn and not realizing he had not more than seven feet to go. He clung to the gunwale with the crook of his knees and escaped with no more than a wet seat. The cow was lifted out safely on this

side and left on a good patch of grass while Bobbie and I took
the men back to the mainland.

She was called Rainbow and has been a good servant to us.
She is never naughty like Bluebell, but is downright bad in one
respect, which is denoted by that sullenness I had seen in her eye.
Rainbow will not let her milk down unless there is food in front
of her, and that food must be something she likes well enough.
Suppose you put nothing for her: well, there will be no milk
and she will stretch her neck round, looking at you with sardonic
interest. Suppose you try hay: any beast gets hay; she will
push it about with her muzzle, get her head under it and throw
it about and eat none. This she will do though she might eat
it gladly either before or after she was being milked. Such a
cow as this has the whip hand of you and as far as I know there
is no way of curing her. She is conscious about it all, so conscious
that it is no good trying Pavlov's technique of breaking down
a conditioned reflex. There are some cows with which you
can gradually cut down the food given under such circumstances
until it is sufficient to leave an empty pail in front of them, but
Rainbow is not to be caught like that. What I have to do is to
find the least sumptuous food that will produce the results and
stick to that or its equivalent for feeding at milking time. You
must never feed anything very attractive like oilcake, or you
have no shots in your locker. What would happen in summer
when you do not feed cake, or in war-time when you cannot?
Rainbow has roots at milking time, and in summer an armful
of new-mown grass or kale. She must have had this habit
since her first calving, but if she had been mine since her heifer
days I should be heartily ashamed of having let her develop it.
The moral is to take the calf away from a heifer before she
so much as sees it and never to give her any feed at milking
time.

Rainbow calved on 14th December, 1940, and looked at
that time as bonny a beast as any man could wish to see. She
had improved in condition, was as sleek as a mole and had such
a bag as I never expected. Her calf was black and a bull, a sore
disappointment to me at that time. Little did I know then
that I was to get six bull calves in succession; in fact, I have
not had a cow calf on the place yet. This calf was a beauty, so

square and deep. I had to have a bull anyway, and as Rainbow showed herself such an outstanding cow I felt I could do no better than rear this Tommy Tittlemouse and use him.

There is some risk in importing cattle from outside the West Highland area to a place like Tanera which is so heavily infested with ticks. These parasites carry the protozoan, which, in the bloodstream of cattle, causes a breaking down of the red blood cells and results in redwater fever. It is better, therefore, to rear your own cattle and your own bull. Even so, the heavy tick infestation of Tanera was too much for Rainbow. She had an attack of the sub-acute phase of the disease in May, 1941, when the ticks are invading grazing animals particularly badly. The illness pulled her down in condition and gave her a staring coat, though her milk did not go down markedly. Her twelve-month record of 845 gallons on war-time feeding gave me great satisfaction. She was mated to her son Tommy as soon as he came fit for service, and I waited a long nine and a half months for a cow calf from this union. Bluebell was already in calf to Tommy and produced a bull, so I felt the chances of a cow calf from Rainbow were pretty good. And when the calf did come it was a big white one with black muzzle, eyelashes, feet and ears—one of my favourite colours in cattle. But it was a bull, and I had a good quarter of an hour's curse.

I was interested to observe Tommy from his birth upwards, for my eyes are now not altogether those of a farmer as they were years ago when many a dozen calves passed through my hands. I am supposed to be a biologist and have some work on the study of animal behaviour to my credit. Tommy was no less interesting as an object of study because he was a farm animal being reared for purely practical ends. As a boy I taught a calf to drink without thinking out the problem, but now I saw it analytically. The calf naturally sucks milk and does not drink, and when it sucks its head is in an upward-reaching position. Now, to be pail-fed, this calf, which has never seen its mother and will only know me as parent, must learn to overcome the instinct of a million years which makes it reach upward and suck. I put my finger in its mouth, the middle finger, simulating a teat, and gently incline its head downwards into a quart of the first milk of the cow. Little Tommy is as yet unsteady on his legs and there is not much of him anyway. He has no experience, only inborn instinct. As soon as his muzzle touches the milk his head jerks up with surprising strength. His little organism revolts at immersing his muzzle in liquid though till a few hours ago he had bathed perpetually in a dark sea of it. We try again, wetting the finger with milk afresh and letting him take the finger for a few moments between his upper lip and questing, experimental tongue. Down, down I draw his head and he sucks perhaps a pint through the gap in his lips each side of my finger. He staggers with exhaustion and gives a tiny grunt.

For three days the finger is necessary to guide his muzzle downwards to the milk, the quantity of which has now risen to a total of a gallon a day given in two or three meals. The finger is gradually withdrawn as he sucks, until the fourth day it is withheld altogether, and after a little time of impatient reaching for it he plunges his muzzle deep into the milk and drinks. The finger is gone for good.

Tommy drinks his milk in a few seconds whereas in nature he would have been sucking away for a long time yet. Something in him belies his full belly: some ritual of those million years has not been fulfilled. So Tommy and every other young calf fed from a pail finds himself some little projection or place in his pen against which he can set his tongue and lips, and having found it he sucks away happily and wriggles his tail for a quarter of an hour. The same sucking place is used time after time, and in the course of four months a board may have had a few square inches quite sucked away.

Tommy is in his little pen five feet square, knowing little of the world, which to him cannot be bigger than the byre itself. Then one day when he is three weeks old I open the door to let him come out and move about this world of the byre. But he has never been out and how can he know this is a door? The fact that there is space where there has formerly been something solid does not convey to his speck of brain that he can walk into that space and through something which is a door. But it is at least the characteristic of the young animal to be inquisitive, and that teller of his brain, his muzzle, goes pushing into space. He almost falls out of the pen into the byre, and then all is strange and Tommy is frightened. He jumps forward on unco-ordinated legs and comes into sharp contact with a wall. More fright. He barges sideways and is further upset by the brick floor, which is strange to his feet. He slips and slithers and comes by chance on to the cows' bed. Ah, here is what to him is firm ground. He stands and holds on as it were.

Yes, there he stands all alone and lonely, legs splayed, his head held uncertainly. One foot is knuckled over at the pastern and the whole limb is trembling. His ribs are heaving and in that byre I can hear his heart pounding. No more for now, I say, and put my hands on him. These he knows as I guide him back to the door of his pen, push him in and turn the snib. And now Tommy is in his little home again which he knows, and becomes immediately a bumptious and cocksure little calf.

Thereafter, each day when the cows are at grass I open the door of the calf-pen and Tommy comes forth boldly. His little games are set ones, just like a child's. There is the pre-liminary romp which follows the same pattern time after time and day after day—round to the cows' bed, kick up the heels; jump; run across to a heap of bedding in the corner and try to climb up it; fail to do so, half fall back but land on the feet; run across to the cows' bed again; kick up the heels—and the same again. Now he is puffed and stands a minute before he goes on to his inquisitive games. These include pushing everything off a bench, curry comb, dandy brush, heavy turnip knife and so on; he pulls a box away from a wall and turns it upside down. I do not *wonder* if I shall have to clear up this litter after his capers each day; I *know* I shall, for he observes a close and constant pattern. Usually when I go to put him in his pen I find him lying quiet on the cows' bed.

Always Tommy is pleased to see me, for I mean food to him and all the companionship he has ever known. I shall never forget how one wet day when he was four months old I went into the byre to write as there were visitors in the house. I curled up in the corner on the dry rushes. Tommy rose from the cows' bed, came over to play with my ears and the corner of the manuscript book, and then, with some effort and great deliberation, he climbed on to the heap of rushes and lay down with a sigh, his weight against my body. Tommy was at peace and began to chew the cud.

Chapter 14

A WILD WINTER

BY August, 1940, the farm work necessary to keep the cows for the winter was pretty well done. The hay was in, the swedes were all singled and hoed, and the plot of cow cabbages was already green all over, showing no brown earth at all. The garden was yielding us a wealth of food, and apart from hoeing there was not much more we could do in it before the winter. My leg was now sound enough to allow me to work with the big boulders and dressed stones still lying in the harbour at the foot of the quay. The derrick was set afresh, and with enthusiasm, for it was nine months since a stone had been moved. Raising the big stones was not the only job to do; there was the accumulation of gravel to move in the bend of the quay where ultimately the boat would lie, and there was the seemingly endless quantity of filling to be thrown up into the middle of the structure, tons and tons of it. We did reach the foundation of the quay at its seaward end, but half-way up the harbour we think there must be several feet of shingle lying above the original level of the harbour floor. A stone there has XII cut in its face, where the edge of the quay is seven feet above the present floor. If there were originally twelve feet of depth at that place there can have been but little dry time in the harbour.

It is the seaweed and the east wind together which are mainly responsible for filling the harbour with unwanted shingle. The bladder wrack fastens to a bit of shingle beyond the foot of the quay and the bladders are almost enough to float the stone; the east wind is sufficient to raise it from its bed when the break of the sea is on it, so that with the rise of the tide stone and weed are washed forward into the harbour. Once there, the bladder wrack slowly rots off because it is now out of its optimum conditions of growth. The stone is left.

The job went ahead slowly for a few days round each spring tide, for we could now work only at low water at such times.

168

Not a day was missed even when visitors came; they were pressed into service and always the response was one of pleasure at joining in the work, especially as it involved playing with water and with pulleys. We ourselves rather lost that feeling, but never quite, of the job being in the nature of play. A man does not really lose his boyish love of playing with a piece of physical construction like this quay, but his dignity demands a little more reasonable excuse for it. Then he is quite happy.

A doctor of medicine rowed over to see us one morning; we had never seen him before, but by lunch-time we were good friends. He had worked with the Eskimos of the Coppermine River area and had sledged into the wild Thelon Sanctuary of North-West Canada where I have long wanted to go. It is not surprising that such a man proved a grand help at the quay in the afternoon when the tide was low. We got the first stone to the final level at the inside end of the quay on that day—a huge Caithness blue mudstone which had lain buried below for perhaps fifty years. That stone has come to be called Blue Martin, in remembrance of this friend of a day who may yet return to find pleasure in the finished work.

Bobbie and I were working alone through October and November because there were no visitors then and Alasdair was at school. Some of the stones were too heavy for us to raise on the chain, which was not intended to lift more than half a ton. Those that were twice this weight had their final bed made ready for them in the afternoon. Then we would lever them with crowbars to the foot of the pole, put the chain about them, lower the pulley block and hitch it to the chain. At each end of the stone a float would be fastened with rope, after which there was nothing else to do until almost high tide when it was practically dark. The great stone would come up easily under water, the floats would be detached and the stone swung into position. Then lower a little, remove the chain, and there it was, needing little more than a touch here and there with the crowbar on the following day. Sometimes the chain blocks would jam when the stone was part way up: the heaviest stone of the lot got jammed three times on its vertical journey of twelve feet, which meant unhitching it to release the blocks and waiting till next day to do it again. This in turn meant working three-quarters of an hour later each day when the tide was high. I remember working waist-deep in the water at the end of the quay on that job, and having to come out and run about every two or three minutes because of the cold.

At last that quay was levelled, and its middle filled and the parapet carried along to the end and half-way along the end. No physical job we have ever done has given me the feeling which the quay did at its finish. There were certainly odd jobs to do yet, concreting the surface and the top of the parapet, but the main fabric was built and as I sat in the window of the little house on the Planestones I could not take my eyes off it. How often had I imagined its shape as I now saw it, when there was only open sea overlying an ugly heap of boulders! I walked the length of the quay in the dark on that first evening not once but half a dozen times, feeling the firmness beneath my feet and enjoying the sight of the water just an inch or two below the level at the end where I leaned over the parapet. It was Sunday, 17th November, 1940, only two and a half years after we had bought the place, and when we had estimated it would take us three years to do it. There was no sense of reaction as when the ideal of years is at last achieved, for in this place of Tigh an Quay there is more to do than we can cope with in our lifetime. The finish of one job merely releases us for the next.

All the same, the quay remains a thing of pride to me, possibly more to me than it does to Bobbie, I being a man; though she, being a woman, should be perpetually proud of it because there cannot be many women in Britain who have equally shared in building a dry-stone construction 80 yards long, 12 feet high at the seaward end and 14 feet wide. Little did we know on that first night it was finished how soon the strength of our work was to be tried by the ordeal of tempest.

We enlarged the house just before Christmas, 1940, by getting another small hut of Canadian red cedar, lined with Cellotex. But we did not attach it to the existing house on the Planestones. It was erected in the garden under the high wall of the main range of buildings and facing north up the garden. What a way to face! I can hear someone saying. I like sun in a place as well as anybody else, but if I have to choose between having

sun and having wind as well, and having no sun and shelter
from the wind, then I go for no wind and put up with the loss
of the sun. I have come to the conclusion that this choice must
be made up here. If your house faces south in the North-West
Highlands it means you get all the terrors of the south-east
wind, the miserable greyness of the south wind and the terrific
gales of south-west weather, which is the commonest of all,
especially in summer. Northerly winds are uncommon except
in early summer when they are fine-weather winds. We are
relatively sheltered from the north wind at Tigh an Quay and
experience little discomfort from it, but with the bulk of Meall
Mor immediately to the south it might be thought we should
be sheltered from the south and open to the north. This place
is not unique : only ten miles away the House of Gruinard faces
due north to the open Minch, yet good timber grows, the
gardens grow verbena, escallonia and many another tender
shrub. The rose trees show no sign of having suffered from
wind. After all, anything here which faces north does get a
good deal of sun in summer, when it rises high to the north-east
and sets well above the north-west.

The Garden House becomes a haven when the searing easterly
and south-easterly gales are blowing, and another good reason
for having it well away from the house on the Planestones was
that it gave our visitors and ourselves much more privacy, a
factor which becomes most necessary on an island or where
your house is small and of wood. Everybody has liked the
Garden House, winter and summer, even with its restricted
view of the sea. It was a great liberation for us in Alasdair's
holidays, and he could go into a tent in summer if a friend
were staying with us. But a year later we were feeling the
pinch again and I found definitely the need of a study where
I could write and leave my stuff lying about if I wished. I
loathe having to tidy up every day because I happen to be
working on the one and only table.

I had done a piece of writing for exactly £50, so I invested
most of it in another red cedar hut which was divided into two,
the smaller part being Alasdair's room and the larger part my
study and office. Other household improvements have been
a large storm porch or annexe (as a Highland hotel would call

it) to the house on the Planestones and another very big one to the Garden House. Oilskins and rubber boots can now lie to hand without littering the little rooms. The study may be a blessing to me but it is equally so for Bobbie, because it has got rid of piles of books, papers, a filing-cabinet and innumerable masculine oddments which she would consider no ornaments to the house. The long and wide fitted bench in the study is a bulkhead which we picked up from the sea near Eilean a' Chleirich. It is of seven-ply wood, faced with Columbian pine. An east wind dried this batten beautifully, and when I had built it into the study I polished it with wax. It is a lovely thing. The window of the study looks forth to the apple trees and over the garden; when I sit in there my eyes rise from work and see the small birds of the land—blackbirds industriously scratching a manure heap flat or making holes in it almost like a rat would; hedgesparrows following in the wake of the blackbirds, going in and out of the holes as if they were caves from which to sing their soft undersong; thrushes perch in the apple trees, singing increasingly from January to June, and the wren and robin are there too. Sometimes the birds scatter and the blackbirds cry with alarm—as well they might, for the sparrowhawk has flashed into the garden seeking a panic-stricken blackbird. This bird cannot see me as she perches for a minute on the top of the apple trees and I enjoy a close look at that fierce, cold face and athletic form. How beautiful is the fine barring across the chest, of brown on a field of cream! I wish the bird were not one of our residents, for we have too few small birds here to spare for the hawk. And when an island loses its stock of small birds it may have to wait over-long for recolonization.

The winter of 1940-41 was hard on our few land birds. It was a winter of east wind with one great blizzard which must have buried many a small creature. It began on the afternoon of 18th January when Bobbie and I were going over to the mainland in the launch. There had been heavy snow the day before, though now it was calm and brilliantly clear in the pale winter sunlight. We left the harbour half-way through the ebb tide, which meant we should hardly get back again before the berth for the launch was dry. But it did seem such a good afternoon.

When we were less than half-way over to Badentarbet Pier we could see big white-capped waves a mile away to the south in the sound of Horse Island, though we were in calm water. And on Ben More there were huge plumes of driven snow flying from the several summits and ridges and shining in the sunlight in amazing beauty. Sea, sky and air—all reached a pinnacle of beauty in that moment, but contemplation of it was not my job. I knew that I gazed upon the coming of savagery of the elements, and did then what I have rarely done before: I turned back, and berthed the launch before the harbour dried. This was not done before the wind was upon us, biting cold and flurrying the dry snow from the quay.

A blizzard in Scotland means east wind, for the snow is never in the physical condition to drive horizontally when the wind is in any other airt. We on the Planestones of Tanera could not rightly experience a blizzard because we are at the very sea's edge facing east. The wind could not carry the snow from the mainland across two miles of sea. But it carried the cold and penetrating power gathered in its journey over the mountains, and up the park the blizzard was real. Our few Shetland wethers kept at home made for an exposed place, thus showing their innate wisdom, for the snow was blown clear and they were not in danger of being buried. A blanket of driven snow was coming off the top of Meall Mor, hurrying eastwards with the sun gleaming through it and lighting the millions of separate seething particles three hundred feet above us.

The low sun died and left the menace of night.

The henhouse at the top of the park, built of turf and stone on a summer's day, was quickly filling with drift and the birds themselves huddled in uncomprehending misery. We picked them up and brought them to the shelter of the ruin and gave them a heavy feed of hot mash for the night.

The mainland was an indistinct blur in the dusk, for the flying snow over there removed all detail of houses and crofting ground near the sea. Our shutters were put up for the night because they saved the windows, but they could do nothing to prevent the terrible noise of sea and the shaking and creaking of the little house. The byre was filling with snow when I went out to milk, and poor little Tommy Tittlemouse, then just over a month old, was black no more, but white the length of his back and telling me he was feeling chilled. I made his pen like a little tent with sacks over the top; then I gave him more rushes for his bed and with wisps of them gave his sides and back a good rubbing.

Each hour or two during the night I went out to the quay to look at the launch. Only by seeing can one learn all the places where a boat may be tied with advantage in such a gale. The morning found us battered and quietened just as the animals outside were; the whole organism seems to lower its activity and perception in order to endure the expected hours of misery. Animals do this better than we do, though the very imagination which makes it harder for us may of itself carry us through with a greater resiliency if the spirit is in command.

After one more day of rather easier wind the weather settled for twenty-four hours. Many of the gullies of the mountains had disappeared under an unbroken carpet of white, and some of the houses at Achiltibuie were half buried. How many sheep, I wondered, were buried beneath that whiteness? It was disastrous.

Three days after this, on 22nd January, we had a hurricane from the east: the gale increased all day, reaching its pitch at high tide at half-past three in the afternoon. The waves broke over the quay and fell into the launch at her berth on the inside bend. Would our dry-stone work on the quay stand up to this bombardment? Ought we to bring the launch up to the head of the harbour and let her dry out there, so that she would be free of the torture of the sea for twelve hours?

Bobbie and I got into our Grenfell suits, thinking we would try to beach the launch within the shelter of the harbour. The water breaking over the quay went through our Grenfells and woollen clothes underneath as if it were solid beads of shot. We hauled the launch alongside the quay almost up to the Planestones, but we had not realized how big the sea was even inside the harbour and what force was in these lessened waves. The keel would have been pounded out of her in a quarter of an hour. So we hauled her back again, fighting the wind this time and finding it no easy job to get ropes fast on bollards and samson post. We ran new ropes from her port side right across the harbour and bent them to projecting rocks and anchors.

Then I noticed Bobbie had lost all activity: her face was blue and expressionless and her hands hung in front of her belly like helpless useless things. I took her by the arm and led her back up the quay. She neither resisted nor responded but came like some quiet broken animal that had no will. I was doing that rare thing, gasping with cold, but because I had had to do more of the heavy work my body had not felt it so badly.

Bobbie came indoors. I lit methylated spirit in the Primus burner cup, put on a quart of water, pulled the wet things off Bobbie and wrapped her in blankets on the settee, ran back to the Primus and gave it fifty pumps or so. Two minutes later the quart of water was singing and poured into the hot-water bottle. This went to Bobbie inside the blankets and another quart went on the stove for tea, which was infused inside another three minutes and cups poured out in four. Bobbie was blue no longer and she was perking up again mentally. Neither she nor I have ever been colder than we were that afternoon, yet as we swallowed that tea I could not help thinking that here were we, able to come in and get warm, while at that very moment there were probably men sitting astride upturned boats in the Atlantic Ocean without hope of warm tea and little of rescue. I think our life on this fringe of the ocean has given Bobbie and me the deepest possible sense of responsibility about the use of imported things, whether petrol, paraffin, flour or wheat. The island years impressed on us most surely the sin of waste, but the war years of trying to make a home on Tanera have been an education in making do on the least possible, in being resourceful and in never taking goods from a needy outside world if we could help it.

The east wind blew hard for well over a third of the total time from January to April, 1941. Such a year was not remembered in these parts. It had still one more surprise for us, a demonstration of what an east wind can do over a mere two miles of sea. Many days of March had been that perfect calm, sunny weather which can be some of the best of the Highland year, but towards the end of the month there were signs of the returning offensive of Auster. He came in increasing strength from the 24th of the month, and on the night of the 26th-27th gave us the most terrible hours we have ever spent in this little wooden house. When I went out in the morning I felt dazed, but things of interest revived me in a very short time. I was seeing things I might not see again—at least I hope I shan't. There were wrinkled crabs in the walled garden, not one but a dozen or so, and some were six inches across the carapace. How on earth did they get there? Then I went into the park and found more crabs and many starfish, and my collie bitch Trimmie found a ballan wrasse, weighing a pound and a half. This fish, and the crabs, are denizens of the sea just below low tide mark, and here they lay about the grass two hundred yards from the high tide mark. I remembered reading as a child how tropical storms sometimes raise water from the sea in such volume as to shower fish on the inhabitants of adjacent shores, but I had never thought to experience the phenomenon in Scotland. Sometimes I wish I could have seen that great disturbance of the waters of the Anchorage which caused this to happen, and at others I feel it was just as well to have been in bed.

A few days later I was telling some men at Polbain about the shower of crabs and fish, and heard then that once before a small shower of herring had come down on Ard-na-goine in a big easterly gale. But no herring weighs one and a half pounds and few are as heavy as some of those crabs which were hurled two hundred yards inland. It was not until low tide that I found a deep wave of gravel had been moved from the bed of the sea and deposited in the mouth of the harbour. Oh! the work in clearing it. When I told an old man on the overshore about this he thought it over well:

"Ah no, Doctor," he said, "that wouldn't be the wind itself, now. I'm thinking it wasn't the wind at all. It was affther being in the nature of an eruption."

I would not need to be much more credulous to believe him.

The garden is not very demonstrative in a Highland March, but the evidences of devastation were obvious on this awful morning. The smaller branches on the eastern side of the old

XX*a*. BORN AND BRED ON TANERA

XX*b*. PAT MURPHY TAKING THE "TRUSTY" TRACTOR OVER A
GLACIAL BOULDER

Then the Director of the Agricultural Engineering Research Institute gave me an opinion on small tractors, plainly doubting their utility, though not on personal experience. But he added a postscript to say he had just had a call from the manufacturer of the *Trusty*, who had said objectively that he thought the Director's opinion unduly pessimistic. I liked that touch of objectivity on the part of a manufacturer and wrote him a long letter explaining where I was, what I was, what Tigh an Quay was like and what was expected of a small tractor. Could it tackle very old ley riddled with roots of rush clumps?

I got the straightest of letters back and a lot of explanatory pamphlets. The manufacturer stuck to the point that the Trusty would go wherever a pair of horses could plough. He went so far as to say if I bought one he would come and give a demonstration of the machine's capabilities. That is confidence. I should have to pay about £175 for the tractor, plough, cultivator, harrows and roller, a lot of money for a man who had had his living cut from under his feet less than eighteen months ago. But I felt if I was going to show it was possible to develop a distinctive crofting husbandry in the West Highlands I must be prepared to be the one to make an expensive experiment. It was war-time, I was not fighting as so many of my friends were, and *Island Years* was showing a surprising vigour in the book market. So I took the plunge.

MacBraynes' kindly allowed their steamer to come into the Anchorage with the tractor on board, on 30th March. It was already too late in the season to get very much ploughing done, but you can contemplate doing things in the West Highlands at which one would be aghast in any other agricultural district. I have seen old ley turned in May and sown with oats about the 20th of the month and there has been a good crop by September. One man I knew of went the length of sowing oats the first week in June, and with a confidence which was justified by results. Such a practice would be more than heresy in a farming district; it would be insanity. It seems that the long daylight of this far North and the moist August is enough to hasten growth so far as to make ripening possible by the end of September.

But I was not to get going at all in the spring of 1941. The captain of the steamer called me inboard to see the machine. One of the long handles of tubular steel was pointing skywards and the engine ports were broken. It was a perfect day and a perfect tide for landing the machine on our quay and I could not expect the steamer to come twice in such good conditions. So I decided to take delivery and have the new parts sent on. This was a time when air-raids were dislocating traffic in England, so I did not curse the railways as I certainly should have done in peace-time; also I thought it hardly fair in such a period to decline delivery. So the Trusty swung out on the steamer's derrick and was lowered gently on to a staging I had put across the coaming of the launch. Unloading on our quay was easy: planks were put from the gunwale to the quay, the launch securely tied fore and aft; the tractor was turned through ninety degrees and wheeled off. Eight and a half hundredweights could not have been moved more easily.

The manufacturer sent me the new parts quickly, but the carburettor had evidently been so much disturbed that I could not get the machine going. It is one of my shortcomings that I cannot understand engines, however much I read the books about them. The principles of their action are plain enough, but not their minute anatomy—which is what counts in making them go. The Trusty lay unused until 5th September, when the manufacturer made good his promise and came this great distance to set me going.

Mr. Reach of Tractors (London) Limited and Pat Murphy the journalist came together. I picked them up in the launch at Badentarbet Pier. I had no need to ask who was the Yorkshireman and who the Irishman, and Reach almost immediately said to me, "Why, you were brought up in Yorkshire," which, of course, is a fact, though only half of me is Yorkshire blood—the romantic half—for it is my sincere contention that the Yorkshireman is a romantic. He will pursue an ideal, and it is no detraction from romance to follow an ideal with acumen and common sense. Reach was a romantic too—full of faith in his invention, which in short was the mode of transmission of power from a small air-cooled engine to a pair of wheels. And he had not looked at the soil of English counties purely as a stuff in which he had to make those tractor wheels go somehow: he had picked up flints and arrowheads and pursued the study of them in relation to the areas where he found them.

Reach and Murphy fell upon the engine and had it going in about five minutes, but I thought the carburettor rather a chancy thing all the same. The machine trotted into the park, leapt an open drain and galloped up the steep slope of Cnoc an-t-Sidhe. That alone was an amazing performance.

"It's all in the balance," said Mr. Reach, "in the distribution of weight."

Then he adjusted the plough and started. It was set far too deep, but at least it showed what the Trusty could do. A wide furrow slice nine inches deep lay inverted on the grass; black and fat it was, and we all marvelled at this soil which is despised the length and breadth of Scotland.

Reach the enthusiast rattled off instructions to me which he had to repeat half a dozen times during the day. It was difficult for me to take them in and at the same time be as wonderstruck as I was watching the soil of Tigh an Quay being turned. We raised the ploughshare and widened the furrow slice so that we were ploughing between four and five inches deep and laying each slice beautifully flat so that no grass was showing through at the edges. The top of Cnoc an-t-Sidhe is the residue of some old-time glacier. Below the first nine inches of soil is a couple of feet of glacial silt in which rest large boulders partly polished by glaciation. The tractor plough soon found the tops of these and we were able to see how the machine checked at them without snatch and went out of gear. Murphy and Alasdair and I went to work with pick and crowbar and raised many a dozen boulders in the course of two days' work. Later we moved some of the really big ones, but some will have to wait for the end of the war and the free use of explosives.

Reach was not satisfied with the performance of the engine, and before the ploughing season of 1942 he sent me a brand new tractor which has run most sweetly. Such is pride in the thing one makes as judged by a Yorkshireman.

"What's the good of me calling it a *Trusty* if it isn't?" says Reach.

These men came those days to demonstrate a tractor, but I could see Tanera was working on them. They had crossed the sea to get here, and found a pioneer job which brought out the boy's spirit in them. The nicest thing they could have said they did say—that they were coming again.

Chapter 15

MAKING DREAMS COME TRUE

DURING that winter of 1940-41 we got the idea that we should have a quiet summer barren of the joy of friends. The war was not very old yet and all of us were still in the serious mood of the past summer when holidays were not things to be associated with the present. But when spring came folk were tired with air-raids and overwork and needed just that break of remoteness which Tanera could give. Letters from friends came increasingly often, asking with some hesitation whether they might come to see us during the summer. There were also letters from people we had never seen who would like to call. Well, it is difficult to "call" in the Highlands: in peace-time a call meant lunch and tea in our part of the world, and it was common for us and our acquaintances to make the double journey of twenty to fifty miles to pay such a visit of courtesy. An island is more difficult to reach than even the scattered households of the North-Western mainland, so when we say we shall be glad for anyone to call, it usually means that our open house extends the traditional Highland hospitality of forty-eight hours. Whether chance acquaintances stay beyond that time is for us to say. Our family has no piper who, on the second morning, can play *Lochiel's Farewell to His Guest* before breakfast, but there are equally courteous ways of achieving the same object.

Bobbie and I tend to grow wide awake to the type of unknown persons who write to us. One such fellow has become a close friend who does not bother now to write to ask when he can come. He just comes and it is always all right. But there are those who write in extravagant terms and some who indulge in self-abasement and want to come and work for no pay—besides bringing a dog. I dislike other people's dogs anyway, and knowing nothing of a person I am not attracted by an offer of work for nothing. The Yorkshireman says, "Owt for nowt's worth nowt"; it would be better for a man to

182

stand proud in knowing he can earn his living. If a man is not worth his living, this island is no place for him. In the words of the old farmer for whom I once worked, "Whoever isn't a help on this place is a hindrance."

A young Irish doctor of medicine came on 2nd April when we were still feeling pretty grey after the terrible gale of 26th-27th March. He and I had corresponded for some time because he happened to be the only man who had done a similar piece of research to my own on the red deer, his work having been done in the Wicklow mountains. He honoured me by breezing in as happily as he did, and I cursed the tricky weather which made us have to take him back a day before he need lest our stretch of sea should make him overstay his army leave.

A week later the same borrowed row-boat brought Geordie Leslie, Lt. R.N. Exigencies of leave prevented him from staying very long either, but a year later he came again for a long leave and has spent four good spells with us now. Here was an example of a man taking a grip on the place—and the place taking a grip of him—quite apart from any personal attraction to us. He had got the idea of what our bit of Tanera stands for. When Geordie comes he takes off his coat and rolls up his sleeves and rightly assumes he has come home. Sometimes he brings a box of rock plants scrounged from his relations and sets about planting them as soon as he gets here. Or he says, "I think we'll get the tractor going and plough that piece today," and we do. Geordie wants to plant a belt of trees in the park, which means they will get planted sooner than if we had decided to do it ourselves. It is Geordie's etching which is reproduced as a frontispiece to this book.

Friends have come in these two years whom we have not seen since the war began. Within a week of each other there came Ivan Hulberd, now married and a Captain in the Army, and Alec and Beryl Valentine much be-blitzed; now there was no mad party in *Southseaman* like the one three years before. They got down to singling carrots and helping us catch Shetland sheep on the islands. When Bobbie's sister and brother-in-law came again, veterans also of the London raids, they took eagerly to work as if such use of the hands was necessary to them. Their work consisted of a barbed-wire fence the whole length of our cliff. Another friend, who had not been farther than a mile from Gower Street throughout the London raids, coming in the dry weather of May, 1941, saw the great quantities of seaweed washed on our shore by the easterly gales. He occupied himself burning the lot and pounding the clinker so that we could use it as a potash dressing on the potatoes. "The last kelp-burner of the Isles, and all that," he said, and ever afterwards has signed his letters James McKelpie.

One girl came from England whose passion was gardening. She was a mistress of her craft. It was something worth while to see those hands dip into earth and touch the roots of plants. She shaped our ideas and taught us much, and got me down to helping her clear that terribly shabby corner of the garden beneath the old buildings. We cleared a dozen cartloads or so of broken slates and crockery, and such weeds as dockens, nettles and fool's parsley. It is now called Miss Muffet's corner, edged with a hedge of cotoneasters and filled with fruit bushes.

Whatever Tanera was doing before the war towards making good talk and fun, it has done much more since in a happy spirit of hard work. There are limits physically to the things Bobbie and I can do together, and the coming of friends is our opportunity to get certain big jobs done; especially so when they have some distinctive ability. The chimney-stacks at either end of the old house and main range of buildings were themselves seven feet high and showing signs of crumbling. And the foot of those chimneys was thirty-six feet above the ground on a gaunt roofless gable. We thought a lot about those chimneys in the big gales. Geordie Leslie and I managed to lower the one above the little house on the Planestones, but I was not man enough for the one at the other end and I would not endanger the life of one of His Majesty's serving officers by letting Geordie try it. It was different when James Fisher the bird-watcher and Alan Pullinger, Editor of the *Climbers' Club Journal*, came for a few days. Alan was a climber, and if he thought it fit to get on top of that chimney above the byre I was satisfied to let him. James Fisher and I acted as labourers, boarding over the byre roof below as a protection and getting ready to clear the rubble. Alan climbed that seven feet of bare chimney and stood on top of it with the calmest skill I have

ever seen.   Then he lowered the stack stone by stone to the
level of the gable, put two flat slabs over the flues and came
down.

Thus has our house been full each summer from March or
April till October, and I believe Tanera has had its place for
these few in healing war-worn bodies and minds.   We have
had fresh food in plenty for them from garden and dairy;
we have seen lines soften in their faces and frames toughen,
and it has been joy for Bobbie and me.   A journey to the islands
to gather the Shetland sheep for clipping or marking makes
a good outing for our friends, and we almost rely on their
help now for the necessary numbers in working the sheep on
to a small promontory where the animals can be caught.   What
happy days they can be, these shepherding trips to the
islands!   They are good, fine, calm days of necessity and the
islands are looking their best.   Perhaps there are six or eight
of us and Trimmie the collie, all able to run.   The sheep are
always troublesome to catch, sometimes a tup puts one of us
on our back or a strong wether drags a fellow along the
slippery rocks to the sea.   What a yell of joy there was when
I fell over backwards into the sea with a struggling sheep
in my arms from the forepeak of the launch!   The sheep
was captured with a boathook and I came round to the stern
of the boat to climb up the rudder.   Clipping is no orderly
business of having a sheep brought to you as you sit astride
a clipping form in comfort.   We have to clip where we can
catch the sheep on the serrated rocks of the steep promontory.
Sometimes a ewe will leap off into the sea, swim across to
the main mass of the island and be lost to us for the year.

Alasdair has grown up to almost fifteen years old in a world
in which these exciting things for a boy are real and serious,
and not play.   The island years of the Clerach, Treshnish and
Rona were not holidays and glimpses for him, but the wholeness
of his life; now on Tanera his school holidays are spent helping
to carve a home and a farm on a rough island.   I believe this
quality of reality in the physical things boys like doing is
important.   Some day we may have a bigger Highland or
island estate, on which we shall consider it part of our social
obligation to have a few lads in the school holidays.

A school friend of Alasdair's had a short spell with us, in which he did one long launch trip to the sheep and for driftwood, and fishing for the pot. Then he helped us ferry over from the mainland a little white heifer I had fancied and bought. His enthusiasm burned as he manfully helped with these manly jobs. Alasdair and he were discussing another schoolfellow one day whose father had a farm in the south of England.

"It will be a much better farm than ours, though," said Alasdair rightly.

"Not a bit," our young friend replied, "*they* haven't got a boat."

In the autumn of 1941 I was sitting on the hillside looking down on our ruin. How different it was from two years before! There were the trim lines of the quay and the Planestones terrace, the increasing amount of dark dug ground in the garden, the greenness of the hill and the attenuation of the rushes in the park. The ruin itself was no great eyesore from up there, neither is it as we live about the walls themselves, but that place we had called the walled garden in an optimistic moment was depressing from wherever it could be seen. As you came up the quay and looked through the arch there were desolation, decrepitude, dockens, ragwort and twitch—a jumble of rubble and weed two or three feet deep over the whole courtyard. The only beautiful thing in there needed looking for, and was a little wild geranium which bloomed nine months of the twelve.

I believed we should feel happier if that place were cleared, but how could we undertake such a job now when so much of our labour must go to immediately productive ends? The walled garden would be a pleasaunce only. Then, as I sat up there looking down on the place as on a plan, I got a new conception of what the walled garden should be. It should be divided into two, the larger part inside the archway being 22 yards by 12 yards and the smaller part near the byre 14 yards by 12 yards. This latter should be the farmyard, and instead of dropping the remaining bit of the factory wall which fell seventy-five years ago, I would build it up and make it the side of an open-fronted haybarn. The guttering of this barn could lead the rainwater to a cistern which, being opposite the byre door, would be useful for watering the cows at night in winter. The south wall of the farmyard could be the back of a lean-to shed for implements.

I knew there was an immense amount of stone in that court-yard, especially where the wall of the many arches had fallen. The removal of the earth, slates and rubble would be job enough without carrying out all the stones as well, which would only make another unsightly heap until I could use them. It would be an economy of labour to make the division between walled garden and farmyard a dry-stone wall five feet high, of the best workmanship I could produce. As the whole court-yard was so long, the walled-garden part would look better for being shortened and bounded by my own dry-stone work.

The decision to undertake a job is the most difficult part of it for me. Now I had taken this decision and felt eager to be getting to the hard work it would entail. Much as I should have liked to begin at the archway and work back, I put that desire aside and began at the farmyard end because that was where the labour would first ease the general working of the farm. I cleared a strip six feet wide right across the place where the new dry-stone wall was to be built, and was delighted to find that below all the rubbish there was an excellent paving. A job of wholesale clearance like this one cannot be undertaken until there is somewhere available for a tip. You cannot waste your time clearing one place and littering up another. We were fortunate in having decided to extend the Planestones terrace southwards across the head of the harbour to our boundary. Any big ugly stones we found which were unsuitable for a dry-stone wall—the sort which the dyker describes in the term that "it wouldna sit in a bog"—we carried or rolled out to use in the extension of the terrace, which was to be several yards wide. The main "eye drain" from the park opened where the terrace was to come, so we built a stone culvert through to the sea. It is our intention, when this terrace is full and the filling well settled, to build a high wall on it which will protect that odd corner of ground, which the old people called the calf park, from the worst of the east wind. We hope to make

a water garden there at the mouth of the drain and grow some
of the royal fern which is so common about the lochs of Eilean
a' Chleirich but is not found on Tanera.

That piece of ground, the calf park, is the foot of the steep
northern slope of Meall Mor and the poorest bit we have. It
is continually wet with seepage from above, and yet it drains
rapidly because the soil is thin and mixed with rock detritus
from the cliffs above. The wind through there is truly terrible
whether east or west. We planted it with a good many trees
of one sort or another, but those which are not already dead
we are moving elsewhere because the wind has reduced them
to thin struggling sticks. A good many crocus corms and cheap
daffodil bulbs have gone in there also and have made a brave
show in 1941 and 1942, but few are showing in 1943. We
can hope for little improvement until this terrace and east wall
are up and the wall to the west raised a few feet. Even then we
shall wonder with what to start in that niggard place; what
we should like would be a wild garden of birch trees, alders,
furze bushes, and crocus and daffodils in season.

Beginning the clearance of the walled garden, then, was also
the beginning of the extended terrace, and we had the double
thrill of seeing the one place coming clean and the other growing.
Perhaps I should say there were three exciting things, for as
I brought to light the big stones of the fallen wall of the arches
I set them as the foundation of the new dry-stone wall across
the courtyard. It was an economy of labour to keep this going
as well. All the small stone from the rubble went into the
middle of that new wall, and when we found our barrows
full of limy soil only, and not of slates and stone, we ran the
loads into the garden instead of to the terrace and thus limed
a big piece of ground in the course of the winter.

The farmyard was cleared by December and my new wall
built. I was satisfied with that dry-stone wall and proud of it.
A mouse could doubtless find a niche big enough in the face
to allow it to escape, but a rat certainly could not, and so well
filled with small stone is the wall inside that the same mouse
would find it difficult going. I had done my best to get any
lichened faces of the stones to the outside so that the finished
job should not look raw.

The winter of 1941-42 was remarkable here for its dryness. This had two distinct effects on the complex of our life : it meant that the labour of clearing the walled garden was much lightened, indeed a wet season like the following winter would have made the work impossible; and the weather meant that I was drawn outside every day. There was so much to do anyway, and so much could be done because the ground was dry, that I worked my fill each day and was too tired to write anything but necessary letters in the evenings. The bank balance dwindled, therefore. If I let my enthusiasm for work overcome my good sense, it would mean an end to the development of this property as a self-contained farm, which was the job I felt it incumbent on me to do as a contribution to solving the West Highland problem.

Bobbie said, now I had built the wall across I could come inside more and get some writing done. I entirely agreed, but laid the foundation of a baffle wall in the walled garden to prevent a straight draught of east wind going into the farmyard, and once the foundation was there my hands would go to the job in every spare moment, so that also was finished and the writing left. But there is always a swing of the pendulum and the intensely wet winter of 1942-43 has enabled me to finish this book and other work as well. Oh, for the spring and fresh air again! And for the end of the war when I shall feel justified in writing outside again on a fine day!

As we reached the eastern corner of the courtyard the rubbish grew deeper, and when we almost reached the wall the paving suddenly stopped. It was the edge of the kiln where peat was burnt to produce the red herrings for which Tanera was famous. The kiln was three feet wide, nearly three feet deep and nine feet long, and even now was full of ash. We mixed this with soil and lime mortar to form the body of what is now a herbaceous bed overlying the kiln and the few feet of paving west of it.

When the wall was finally cleared there still remained the foundations of the piers of masonry which had supported the wall of the arches which fell so long ago.

If the foundations could be got out without too much damage to the paving round about, the holes could be made into flower-beds, 8 feet by 2 feet 6 inches. The stones were very big ones, well mortared in and deep, but we got them out in time and used them as the first courses of other baffles which we have built against the wall of the main range of buildings to check the sweep of east wind through the archway. At last those holes were filled with good earth, the flagging of all that court-yard well brushed with a hard broom during a heavy rain, and the order had been given for some standard rose trees which were to form a line in this row of beds where the foundations had been. I moved an Albertin rose which had not done very well on the Planestones and set it against my new transverse wall, and an Excelsior rambler was put by the main baffle. Bobbie and I agreed that we needed one good standard tree of some kind in the middle of the walled garden, or courtyard as it looked now. A flowering cherry would probably die, a weeping willow or wych elm was hardly the right thing, nor was a standard fruit tree. We decided on a sycamore as being hardy and likely to form a compact close-topped tree. The nurserymen unfortunately sent us a bad tree—eight feet of stick and three little twigs at the top. This we endured for six months and then replaced it with a handsome specimen laburnum which I chose for myself when in Inverness.

The standard rose trees were another disappointment. They came late, unheralded by an advice note, and had spent a fortnight on the journey. The weather was intensely dry at the time, so they reached us in a desiccated condition from which we were unable to revive them. The nurserymen have now replaced them and we have added a few more rambler roses which are intended to adorn the walls. Once more we are being optimistic, but this time conditions for the growth of these trees are as good as we can make them. We have even planted a fan-trained apricot tree against the wall of the house facing south and flanked by a baffle wall to east and west. I have heard of this courtyard being called the hottest place in Coigach, and if apricots were grown here a hundred and fifty years ago, why not now? Perhaps we are at a stage in the cycle of weather when it is worsening, when there is more east wind than there was a century ago. Certain it is that all the plum and apricot trees have been gone many a long year, and in the few years we have had Tigh an Quay the old apple trees have tended to lose some of their canopy rather than add to it.

Several of our friends have brought rock plants which we have put in the interstices of the paving of the courtyard. Dwarf phloxes, saxifrages, tiny irises and aubretias will gradually fill those earthy niches and the dockens and annual poa grass will come no more. Desolation has left the place and we feel no shame now as we come up the quay with friends and look through the arch. The immensity of the job of clearing has but added to our enjoyment of this separate and distinctive garden.

Birds seem to love it though the plant cover in there must necessarily remain sparse. Bird song sounds loud there and the many holes in the walls are an attraction to thrushes, pied wagtails and hedgesparrows. The robin has nested here in 1943, for the first time since we came. The former habit of these birds was to leave us in March and return in October. It is for the sake of the birds about the farmyard and walled garden that I have had reluctantly to part with the cat—for which particular cat I had a high regard.

She came to us in this way. During the winter of 1940-41 Bobbie called me into the dairy one day to look at a pan of milk of which the cream had been disturbed. Was it a rat? No, but I could not see how it could be a cat as there was no such animal here on our side of the island. I reserved judgement. Then one day after a night of rain the cream was disturbed again and on the bench where the pans were set were several little round footmarks. It was certainly a cat; and another day I found those prints on a bit of soft smooth earth. But we never saw the cat. Various contraptions of fish netting failed either to catch the cat or prevent her going into the dairy. Cats tread delicately and with precision.

The trouble went on until July, at which time I had two tons of baled hay at the back of the byre. My mother had sent gooseberries to Bobbie by post, which meant they were rather the worse for wear when they reached us. Bobbie laid them out on dishes and newspapers on the lower tier of bales in the byre because she had so little room in the house. As she worked there she heard a loud purring but thought it must be the muffled sound of a starling on the chimney-stack above the byre. Then she looked up and saw a tortoiseshell-and-white face keeking over the uppermost bales of hay. Bobbie quietly left the byre and fetched me.

"I've found the cat," she said.

To say she had "found" the cat gave me the notion it must be dead, for surely such an elusive animal would merely have been "seen" for a momentary glimpse. But no, she had found the cat and it was alive. The face was still there when I came in and all my animosity to the creature evaporated. I saw the cat now as a homeless thing which much wanted a home but was in doubt about asking for one.

"Ah, little pussy," I said, and climbed on to the first tier of bales. The cat recognized the kindliness I was extending; she stood up and reached forward her head to my uplifted hand.

What purring!

And what a cat!

She was immense. She was tortoiseshell and white in colour and had a coat in glorious condition. Not a fluffy coat but a short one through which the rippling movements of her muscles gleamed as she strode to and fro in her sudden pleasure. I watched her in admiration. Here was a real cat, embodying and expressing the whole notion of cat, and she was beautiful. How long were her legs, how clean her rib and body line; how surely was each foot put down! Bobbie fetched a saucer of milk and the cat came down to the first tier of hay, still purring her pleasure.

Here was an animal which had been about the place for six months and had most carefully avoided being seen by us. Apart from the milk she had taken she had hunted her food and had become to all intents and purposes wild. Now she had decided to be seen, and having shown herself had thrown off completely all idea of shyness or hiding.

The cat said, "Here is my place and I will stay with you."

And I said, "Stay you shall until I see you catch a bird in this garden and then you will go."

Had we been living on the mainland I would have given her some little licence with the birds, though not much, because there is a continuity there: but on an island where there are no

XXIIb. FELLING THE UNSAFE CHIMNEY STACK
(see page 184)

XXIIa. THE WALLED GARDEN
(compare with Plate IVb)

low. It might have been the three hard winters which had reduced them—or it might be the cat. I could not blame her yet. And then in April I found her with a chaffinch, a species of which we had very few. Then I found a few more feathers on top of the hay. It was no good being sentimental. I put Miss Purcell in an openly woven sack and took her to the mainland. She neither struggled nor complained, which made it all the harder for me. I went to a collection of rabbit-holes in some rocks and put the cat down there. She strode with all her characteristic precision and purposefulness into the largest hole and disappeared. That was the last I saw of her. Rabbits, I fancy, were more desirable game to her than small birds. I missed her, and still do; and perhaps this year, when rats are common about the place as a result of my corn-growing operations, she would have had game enough without the birds. But I have made the final decision not to have a cat here again. The birds are much more numerous now and far tamer than before. And small birds collectively will do more good about this place than a cat, and give much more pleasure. I have been going for the rats with break-back traps and find them most efficient, but more rats pour in from the cliffs as fast as I clear them about the buildings.

As far as I can see, there is no sure way of clearing rats out of an island. The animals are great travellers and are not dependent on food produced by human beings for their sustenance. Their diet is varied and plentiful and the animals seem well aware of the seasonal crops of food to be had in various places. The sheltered shore is their great stand-by. At low tide they can move about among the weed and find little crabs and shellfish whether it is winter or summer. Springtime provides them with plenty of dead sheep, which they tackle in the night when the ravens and great black-backed gulls have had their fill by day.

One sheep died in the shelter of a small chasm about fifty yards from the sea at the back of Tanera and was not pulled to pieces by the birds there, for they are too wary to go into such an enclosed place. Thus the carcass was still more or less intact when the greenbottle and bluebottle flies came on the scene in June. The flies laid their eggs on the carcass, the maggots ate much of it and pupated. And that was where the rats came in. They made a beautifully defined little track into the chasm from the cairn of rocks at the seashore, and another little track led out on the landward side. The rats feasted on these luscious morsels which were the pupae of the blowflies and made no further inroads on the bony recesses of the skeleton.

The Arctic terns nest on the little island in the Anchorage and on the rock to the north of Eilean na Saille, north-west of Tanera. The rats know this too and journey to the rocks when the terns arrive. It seems that rats can tackle the job of egg-stealing from birds the size of terns despite the combative powers of this particular species, but birds the size of herring gulls, and their eggs, are apparently immune. Ducks' eggs are also left alone, though the ducklings are eagerly sought by the rats. The rodents have prevented the terns breeding on Tanera for two years of the four we have been here. Some of the common gulls' nests on the larger island in the Anchorage are robbed by rats, but these birds always manage to rear a crop of young ones.

The late summer brings the rats into the corn and potatoes. Definite runs up to two hundred yards long are traceable from the dykes into the growing corn. I do not know whether the rats carry corn away and make stores, but their industry with potatoes is amazing. I have seen caches of potatoes weighing up to twenty pounds thirty or forty yards away from the nearest row.

The art of clearing a place of rats appears to lie in persuading the whole population to feed on food which you put down for them. This takes time, but when this stage is achieved the food may be mixed with pure white arsenic and deaths are 100 per cent. Tanera is over eight hundred acres in extent, and all the islands at the back as far afield as Tanera Beag are infested. If the whole group of islands were being incorporated into a wild-life sanctuary I think it would be worth while tackling the rat problem here as an experiment in extermination under peculiar conditions. A whole winter might be given to the campaign and a ton or two of wheat would be necessary for bait.

An increase in the population of buzzards in this area is greatly to be desired. Unfortunately, the ravens have bullied the buzzards so much that they have not nested on Tanera since 1940. The ravens themselves are not great ratters. When I began my break-back trapping in the autumn of 1942 I threw the carcasses on the rocks of Fank Point so that I could see from the house if anything came to take them. The ravens were there within a quarter of an hour and cleaned a dozen or twenty rats each morning for three days in succession. But on the fourth they left them alone and never touched them afterwards. No poison was being used.

The rats of Tanera and the Summer Isles are the brown species, *R. norvegicus*. Their hair is rather longer than that of Lowland specimens and their bellies are white. Murdo Macleod, who was born on Tanera, has told me that mass migrations of rats have been seen in the course of swimming the sound between Tanera and the mainland, though he cannot tell me which way they were going. As a guess, I should say they were making *for* the mainland, as the islands present more possibilities as a nursery. Murdo also told me that a plague of black rats occurred about thirty years ago but did not last long. No black rats are found now, which fact is understandable. The black rat is much more mouse-like in that it prefers dry conditions, which an uninhabited Northern island could not supply.

The open-fronted barn which we built in the farmyard has unfortunately helped to make a resident club for the rats. It has held six tons of oat sheaves and hay this year and I have had to keep going regularly with the traps to keep the pests within bounds. Despite the need, there is really no compulsion or co-ordination in the control of rats. Whatever I do here I am only stemming the tide against my own place and I have no power to prevent rat-killing creatures from being shot either on Tanera or the adjacent mainland. Like many other pieces of legislation, the control of rats receives lip service only in the Highlands.

Chapter 16

TOWARDS A HIGHLAND
AGRICULTURE

THE West Highland problem is one of long standing.
Many politicians, but few statesmen, have given attention
to it in moments of political fervour, but not in later
periods of administrative office. The problem is a perennial
boon to journalists: it is so easy to twang the heart-strings
with half-baked observations on West Highland economy, for
the background is emotional and picturesque, with remarkable
nostalgic or evocative quality for readers at a distance—at which
most of them are. It is the perfect example of the social problem
on which everyone considers himself a pundit but which has
received little detailed investigation by anybody. The most
vocal elements are to be found among people living in towns
or places far removed from the Highlands and Islands themselves.

There is always an excellent Aunt Sally for the jousters and
champions of the Highlands in that administrative body known
as the Department of Agriculture for Scotland, which has
responsibilities unknown to its sister the Ministry of Agriculture
in England. The Department is the administrator of the peasant
districts of the Highlands and Islands to an extent far beyond
that of the County Councils concerned. The Department is
sociological and constructive in the engineering sense as well as
agricultural: it grants long-term loans to crofters to improve
their holdings (which practically always boils down to improving
their houses); it builds piers; it provides bulls at no capital
charge, rams for a very low price, and seed potatoes and oats
at a much reduced rate. The Department is an almost almighty
aunt and can stand a good deal of buffeting. There is only one
objection to taking three shies at her, which are the privilege
of everyone who has paid his taxes, and that is she cannot hit
back in the way of answering criticism or defending policy.
She just goes ahead in her all-pervading way. The critic of the

197

Department has one great responsibility and one obligation, that he shall be fair and that for every destructive remark he shall offer a constructive alternative.

The root of the West Highland problem must be sought historically. It lies partly in the break-up of a social system—the clan system—in the eighteenth century, followed by the movement and complete disruption of populations during the period of the Clearances in the first half of the nineteenth century. Poverty of the soil has had little to do with the agricultural side of the depression.

The break-up of the patriarchal clan system deprived the common folk of the glens of their right of being and of protection in that place. The chiefs, scarcely that even in name then, tended to become absentees from their estates, and found themselves desperately in need of money to maintain their status in the more expensive atmosphere of the South. They were no longer warriors with a responsibility to their folk, and began to look upon the people as a capital asset on which they must realize if necessary. One Hebridean chief actually stated that he considered it his right to exploit his estate and his people to his most favourable advantage.

It must be understood that there has never been a middle class in the Highlands, the middle class to which most of us belong; which most of us deride in all sorts of disparaging remarks, but which, at bottom, we know to have an invaluable influence in civilizing human communities. The middle classes are neither the rulers nor the ruled but the great well of free men. There is still no considerable middle class in the Highlands and the standard of civilization is low, consisting of rulers and ruled. If the rulers did rule, in the way that they would willingly relinquish rule when conditions permitted, good might come to the countryside as a whole, but the majority of this land-owning, ruling class is absent from the Highlands and administers its estates through Lowland lawyers whose criterion is the profit and loss account and who have no knowledge of agriculture or sociology.

The sharp division of class between gentry and crofters has resulted in the common folk of the Highlands being devoid of the power of leadership. I believe this lack of ability to initiate and lead is one of the main reasons for the continuing lassitude and mounting depression. Perhaps I am not quite certain whether the lack of *desire* to lead justifies my saying there is lack of *ability*. The present war offers an interesting example of this point : here are these magnificent soldiers from the glens and sea coast who have an intelligence far above the average English recruit. But how many of them have become officers in the course of the war ? Any English or Lowland shop assistant, clerk or mechanic has a good chance of becoming an officer if his address and manner are good and his brains average. The splendid Highlandman rises as far as sergeant-major and rarely dreams of going on to commissioned rank. His own officers are for the most part his own ruling class, and they do not think, either, to push their men forward and lose them to another regiment.

Absence of leadership is apparent in the life of the crofting townships, which are not comparable with the English village, in which division of labour is marked and where leadership rests in squire and church and a few of the villagers on a democratic basis. A crofting township is a collection of individuals, most of whom have similar attainments. Each man can build his house, shepherd his sheep or sail his boat, and remains an individual with little part in corporate life. The Presbyterian churches (for there are three) in the Highlands do not exercise leadership or co-ordinate social effort. The schools teach reading, writing and arithmetic. The Department of Agriculture becomes more and more the administrator of the crofting areas, but, being remote and impersonal and sticking to the bare terms of its job of administrating, it does not exercise the influence it might in developing a communal life in the Highlands. Once a Highlander is transplanted from his native soil his innate ability often advances him along the social scale; his children receive wider education and do not grow up feeling they are the ruled class. They enter the professions as equals with their fellows and rise because they have good brains. The problem remains of how to set free this real ability in the crofting areas and create an active and healthy social organism. It will probably have to start in the schools, where the foundation of co-operative and civic behaviour can be laid.

Another historical factor which has profoundly influenced the destiny of the Highlands has been the coming of the sheep, between the years 1780 and 1850. The pastoral economy before that time was based on a cattle husbandry. Large herds of hardy, slow-maturing cattle were kept. They lived outside all the year round and got little or no keep but a bite of soft hay in the worst of the winter. Strong two- and three-year-old bullocks and heifers were driven to the Lowlands and to England each year to be finished on richer pastures. The story of Highland cattle droving is a romance yet to be told.

Cattle grazing kept the hill pastures from developing a dense mat of decaying herbage, and the hills were evenly grazed through the practice of the people taking the cattle to the higher reaches in the summer. They themselves brought their few pots and pans to the little turf and stone huts called shielings which they built on the high ground to live in while the grass lasted. Oatmeal, milk and milk products were practically their whole sustenance. There were still considerable areas of natural woodland, mainly birch, for by 1780 most of the pine forests had gone to feed the iron-smelting industry. The cattle grazed through these open woods without curtailing them or lessening the fertility of the ground.

Then the possibility of big profits from imported sheep became apparent as the Highlands were quietened. The Clearances began and were prosecuted to establish sheep farms far more than they were to make deer forests. Farmers from the Border country trekked north with their Blackface and Cheviot sheep. The Highlanders had but few sheep of their own and what there were appear to have been of the same primitive type as that of the present Shetland breed. They soon became extinct.

Sheep farming requires cleared ground. It began in the Highlands by reaping the fertility let loose by the felling of the pine forests and was maintained at a highly profitable level by clearing great areas of birch scrub. The cattle population declined far more rapidly than that of the people, which was bad enough. The fertility of hill ground cannot be maintained without the presence of cattle which clear the mat and tread it and muck it. Sheep are more selective grazers and are much harder on forest growth. The nineteenth century saw a gradual decline in the profits of West Highland sheep farming and the twentieth century has seen it become an acutely depressed industry. It can never revive to its old state, for the industry has lived on the capital of fertility in the hill grazings for a hundred and fifty years and it is nearly gone. Every sheep which has walked off has taken lime and phosphates away, a process hastened by the development of the lamb trade in the last forty years. A mountainous countryside cleared of forest growth soon loses the fertility by erosion, which again is hastened in the West Highlands where the rainfall is high. Cattle, of course, take away lime and phosphates also, but their drain on the capital of fertility was less because of their grazing habit and the fact that they were not so inimical to forest growth.

The Highlanders took easily to the husbandry of sheep. It was pastoral rather than agricultural, which they much preferred. Farming on arable lines is disliked by the average Highlander. The large numbers of cattle of the old days were used by the people to manure their arable fields by the simple expedient of grazing the cattle on the hill by day and putting them in the parks at night in winter or early spring. The husbandry of sheep by the crofters has resulted in a downward spiral of infertility of the already limited arable land.

The sheep are not hardy enough to remain on the hill all the year round now that so much of the fertility has leached away. The ewe stock has to be brought into the parks in spring, which much delays the ploughing and results in a late straw crop. This in turn means less winter keep, so fewer cattle can be wintered and there is less manure for the ground the year after.

There are now large areas of the West Highlands where winter milk is a great rarity, a fact which alone greatly detracts from the standard of nutrition and makes the people more dependent on the outside world. All the West Highlands produce is the rawest of raw material in the shape of lambs of poor quality (but which do well on Southern grazings) and weaned calves of better quality (but still raw unfinished beasts). The prices obtained are low, at the very bottom of the agricultural ladder, but the things which come in, whether food, clothes or furniture, are highly manufactured goods with high transport charges, and are sold at the highest retail price. The growing lack of self-sufficiency leaves a gap which the Highland crofter has so far been unable to bridge, so he has come to depend on all manner of subsidies and State help not available to the ordinary farmer. He is the privileged class within the nation, for he is the one type of landholder who cannot be evicted for bad husbandry or made to work his land better. The war has seen a deterioration of arable cultivation on the already low level of 1939.

The crofter is to a large extent unable to help himself for he and his like form Britain's only primitive peasant community, situated on the fringe of a highly industrialized country. Laws are made for the majority of which the crofters are not a part. How can he find his feet and at least stabilize his population? The West Highlands have still to throw up a leader who can help to shape their economy as Horace Plunkett did in Ireland.

Much as must remain to be done by State action, it is my belief that the crofter can do much to better his standard of living by his own efforts, backed by knowledge he certainly does not possess at the present time. His crofting husbandry of a very small area of arable ground is not adapted to help his own family table, but follows the rough extensive husbandry of the Highland sheep farm. The crofter has little income and few outgoings; therefore his cultivations should be partly designed to keep his table self-sufficient. He was well fed in the old days, although sparsely. Now his belly is well filled but he is ill fed. Very little fresh sea-fish is eaten because little is being caught on the West Highland seaboard. Few, if any, West Highland oats are being threshed and milled for human consumption, though oatmeal does still play a large part in the people's nutrition.

White bread of peculiar baking is now the main cereal food of the West Highlander. This bread comes from Glasgow in crates, and at this time of the war must be a considerable item of transport strain. It has to travel long distances along relatively slow lines of communication so the water content is initially very high. The top of the loaf is dark brown and hard and tough; the sole of the loaf is pale and still harder and tougher. The sides and butt ends of the loaf are white and soft. The doughy, watery middle can be compressed to very little because the bread has no substance. When about three days old, that is, when it is in full circulation, the butts of the loaves go mouldy despite the fact that before the war they were expensively wrapped in waxed paper on which was printed the soothing information that the bread was "untouched by hand". It is poor stuff, but the people liked it. One man told me that when it first came into the countryside it seemed so nice he could eat it "like cake", without the butter. Even the new National flour looks poor stuff when it reaches the West as bread which is still only "off white".

Very little butter and cheese is made now in the West Highlands, though some islands like Islay, Coll and Tiree are exceptions. It is in the Northern Highlands that the standard of nutrition has sunk lowest. Winter milk comes out of a tin. Potatoes are one of the main foods and are generally properly cooked in their skins. Green vegetables other than occasional cabbages are almost unknown. Salt herring are still eaten, but in less quantity than heretofore.

It is very generally assumed that the climate of the West Highlands is so bad as to make the cultivation of human vegetable food either impossible or unprofitable, and that the soil is too poor anyway to do much towards improvement. My own attitude is to consider the West Highland countryside as one of the favoured ones in Britain, and the poverty of the soil is nothing to be greatly discouraged about, for soil can be made productive if the climate allows good growth.

What are the factors of climate in the crofting areas, which, it must always be understood, are on the coastal strip and never far from sea-level? Altitude and proximity to the sea are so important in governing climate in the Scottish Highlands that no general picture can be taken as the one typifying this coastal strip where the crofts lie. First, there is the temperature and the range between summer and winter temperature: the annual mean temperature of the West Highland coast is exceeded only by that of the coastal strip of the south of England and southern Ireland. Our summer mean temperature is 55°-57° F. compared with 60°-63° F. in the Midlands and south of England; the mean winter temperatures are 40°-42° F. compared with 38°-40° F. in a large part of England. The annual range of mean temperature on the West Highland coastal strip is only 14°-16° F. The range in Kent is 24° F.

The West Highlands are the rainiest district of Britain, reaching the pitch of an average of 165 inches a year at Loch Quoich in western Inverness-shire. But here again it does not apply to the coastal strip. The annual average of the greater part of the West Highland coast is about 50-55 inches, and here in north-west Ross-shire and Sutherland it is only 40-45 inches. The summer rate of evaporation on the coast is also high.

Snow falls comparatively rarely on the narrow coastal strip, and when it does fall it does not lie more than a few hours, or at most two or three days as in the extreme winter of 1940-41. Here on Tanera we had no snow at sea-level in the winter of 1941-42 and our lowest temperature that winter was 26° F. in the first week of March. I am writing now towards the end of February, 1943, when we have not yet had more than two degrees of frost. Late frosts are very rare. There was a severe one in May, 1935, at Dundonnell, but that is two and a half miles inland, and I am sorry to say I did not make a special journey to the sea then to note what had happened there.

This extremely equable and mild climate does not extend far inland, not more than a mile or two, because the mountains rise suddenly and the sea's ameliorating influence is soon lost, so it is quite common to have glorious weather, dry workable soil and grass growing at sea-level in March and April while an almost Arctic climate continues at 1250 feet—snow lying frozen and the roads blocked to traffic at their summits.

The climatic factors mentioned so far show the West to have weather favourable to luxuriant plant growth. But there is one very powerful limiting factor—wind. The West Highlands are in the principal storm track of the British Isles, the belt which begins in mid-Atlantic, sweeps north-eastwards to catch the north-west of Ireland and the Hebridean and north-west Highland coasts and goes on to the Arctic, missing Norway in its most extreme severity, but turning northwards and almost north-westwards again to give the south of Iceland a good buffeting. The wind here is terrible. It would be grossly unscientific of me to attempt to lessen its importance on plant growth because I am enthusiastic as to what can be done. But

I will say that wind is not all-powerful in the face of man's ingenuity—and hard labour.

Even without wind shelter it is possible to grow good and plentiful grass, for the climate of the West is otherwise perfect for this basic food of stock. It is a problem of soil treatment to which I shall come in a moment. The climate apart from the wind happens to be a good one also for the culture of most vegetables and fodder crops. Shelter must be made somehow. Individuals, even ones without much money but not severely pressed for time, can do much towards the beginnings of shelter by such means as making dry-stone dykes or low windbreaks of turf. A quarter of an acre of walled garden will grow a good deal of vegetables and fruit. Two-foot earthworks running north and south and twenty to twenty-five yards apart on open ground will also allow things to grow without overmuch hindrance from wind.

But the provision of shelter to the crofting townships, with their plethora of gimcrack barbed-wire and bedstead fences which provide no windbrake, is a job for the State and the landlords together. It should be put plainly to the crofters that the loss of a small percentage of the nearest common grazing would be more than made up by the shelter which a ring of trees planted there could give to a township. A wide belt of trees would add much to the appearance of a township, though the plea of amenity would cut no ice with the average West Highlander who, with so much beauty round him, seems indifferent to the squalid appearance of many crofts and townships. As the trees grew they would provide fencing timber for the crofts. This in itself would be a great asset, for little agricultural improvement is possible without ample fencing. The shelter belts of timber would often be uneconomic as timber, but their value would have to be judged in a social sense over a long period of years.

The wind is so strong on the coast that the choice of shelter timber is itself a problem. It is generally supposed that the mountain pine will grow right down to the shoreline, and is excellent for the first three or four rows of a windbreak. We have lost about two-thirds of those we planted in our cliff, those in the deeper pockets of the soil having died sooner than those in pure peat. We also tried two hundred Corsican pines, of which there is none now left at all. Norwegian spruce burns badly with the salt spray, and the Scots pine grows but poorly at the sea's edge. It is my belief that Sitka spruce will be the best tree for the first few rows, then Douglas firs, followed by Scots pine or larch. Sitka spruce has the additional virtue of being relatively proof against rabbits. All cover timber and shrubs in this part of the world need to be planted much closer than the books say or the wind will lick round them and kill them. This is expensive at the time of planting as well as in after-care.

Once land has shelter in the West Highlands the culture of soft fruit and stone fruit becomes easy. Black-currants give an enormous crop if well mulched with seaweed. Stone fruit does well against walls. It is our intention to begin fruit culture on cordons, as this method would tend to mass the trees and allow of greater control of the wind factor.

A biologist living in the Highlands, and especially the Islands, for any length of time, becomes acutely aware of the value of vegetational cover and sees it as a national asset to be conserved rather than as an individual possession to be exploited. This countryside was originally well furnished, even as late as 1549, when Dean Munro described Gruinard Island (eight miles from Tanera) as being covered with birch trees. Now there is not so much as a shrub of any kind. Once cover has gone it is very difficult to get back. We, with our few island acres, realize this most painfully.

Let us look at the nature of the soil in its relation to growing such crops as will raise the standard of nutrition in West Highland homes. Judged as a whole, the soil is poor and rather light, though in some volcanic areas the soil is rich and loamy. I shall not forget how struck I was with the character of the soil as it was caught up in some pockets of the rock on Lunga of the Treshnish Isles. I believe it would have been perfect for early or forced crops if it could have been carried to a sheltered site. The grass on that island was rich and plentiful despite the rabbits. The islands of Canna and Muck and part of Ardnamurchan also enjoy this rich soil of volcanic origin. We in the North-West have the poorest soils in Scotland, weathered through the ages from the Torridonian Sandstone, quartzite and Archaean gneiss. In addition, much of our ground up here is covered with peat—or moss as an earlier generation called it—which is proverbially slow to release its chemically and physically locked-up plant food.

The fact that the soil here is intrinsically poor has made the reclamation of our ground all the more interesting, for we cannot be said to have started with advantages over other parts of the Highlands. There is really no need to have our soil analysed to tell us it is short of lime and phosphates. We know it; 99.9 per cent. of West Highland soil is in a condition of shortage of these essential plant foods, but the soils of the North-West are shorter still. Whatever else we may or may not do, there can be no agricultural revival or rehabilitation in the West Highlands until the limited arable ground at least is dressed adequately with lime and phosphates. It is impossible to get good crops and economically growing stock from land so utterly deficient in these plant foods. It would be waste of effort to drain and cultivate the land unless they were supplied.

There are ample deposits of calcium carbonate in the Highlands which could be applied to the soil immediately without going to the trouble of burning it to drive off the carbonic acid and produce quicklime. All lime comes back to the condition of calcium carbonate before it is available to the plant as food, but if it has re-formed from quicklime the carbonate is in an extremely fine state of division and therefore more readily available. The calcium carbonate deposits to which I refer are the beaches of shell sand, and those fewer beaches of coral sand which can be worked at low spring tides. The only objection to using these immense stores of calcium carbonate in their present condition is that a larger quantity must be applied. But even that objection has its bright side when it is remembered that an initial heavy dressing of ten tons to the acre will last twenty years, whereas a dressing of half a ton of quicklime to the acre lasts but the one growing season. Lucky is the coastal crofter who can carry shell or coral sand for himself and dress the whole of his few acres of enclosed ground within two or three years. He has laid the basis of success with little expenditure other than his own labour.

The Government pays a 50 per cent. subsidy on the cost of
lime applied to agricultural land. By this means a crofter could
actually add to his income if he cared because he would be being
paid for his labour. Here in the Summer Isles there is the deposit
of coral sand in the sound between Tanera Beag and Eilean Fada.
Thousands of tons were taken from there in the old days and
it was spread on the land "just so thick as you could write your
name in it", as Murdo Macleod has told me. Bobbie and I
have been at the same game, and the fact that we lost a dinghy
while engaged in it was largely our own fault. We can carry
two tons at a trip in the launch at a running cost of a gallon
of petrol and a pint of oil and the wear and tear on the launch.
Five shillings, say, for two tons—and the rest of it is our certainly
considerable labour. As a matter of personal pride we have
not called on the Government for the half-cost. The shell
sand of the Outer Isles was being put ashore on this side of the
Minch at eleven shillings a ton before the war, a price at which
it was well worth while applying, but the pity was there was
very little coming over. As a policy for the West Highlands,
then, a supply of the ever-essential lime is available within the
area at reasonable cost and at little expense of transport to the
nation.

There are also deposits of limestone—calcium carbonate in
the form of solid rock—which were quarried and burnt in
earlier years. One such deposit was communally worked by
the crofters with the co-operation of the Estate in Strath Kan-
naird, a few miles from here nearer Ullapool. The kilns were
fired by peat fuel and I have been told that the peat dug by a
family in one day would be considered enough to burn the
lime necessary for the croft each year. Once more, the job is
capable of being carried out within the countryside without
expensive transport or gear from outside.

Phosphates are more difficult: it has been reasonably put
forward that the increase and maintenance of mankind and his
civilizations may yet break down because the limited world
supply of phosphates is being squandered. If a soil is deficient
in phosphates there is no way of getting them there in the way
that nitrogenous matter can be generated in the soil biologically.
The cheapest form of phosphate at present is basic slag, a by-

XXIV. HARVESTING AT TIGH AN QUAY
(compare with Plate II)

lesser extent on the islands just behind us. They were to be seen on Ard-na-goine from late October to April, but never on our ground. It was unlikely that they would come, I thought, for wild geese would not choose a narrow glen from which they might have difficulty in getting away quickly if surprised. Murdo Macleod told me they never came to our place in his day.

But they came in the winter of 1941-42 and again in 1942-43, at first hesitant and wild, and then with a growing confidence in the sanctuary we offered them. They grazed over the clover of the hill, came on to the little green by the sea, then into the park, and finally a dozen of them decided to have the garden. The main flock came to allow me within fifty yards of them as long as I remained still, but the garden group would let me wheel a barrow within twenty yards of them. An improved grazing first attracted them to us, the peace we offered caused them to stay, and a new rhythm for one flock of wild geese has been established.

What a joy they are to us! As we lie in our beds of a calm night we hear their calling, which is one of the exciting sounds to the human ear; then there is a sudden silence in which we know they are pitching to the grass; a sound of many wings as they land, silence again, and then the small sounds of conversation among them. They come in the day-time too, when the waving, weaving pattern of the flock in the air as they hang on the wind before pitching is a sight which makes us straighten our backs from work. When the flock rises suddenly from the amphitheatre of our park, the acoustic qualities of the place allow us to hear the uprush of sound of wings as if it were an orchestra or a great roll of drums; we hear it analytically and yet as a synthesis, as we could never hope to do on an open *machair*. The grazing barnacle geese remind me irresistibly of a herd of red deer moving across a hillside. There is the same coherent quality of the group in them, the constant raising of a long neck from which an alert head is seeing all. There are the little bickerings of individuals and the same undercurrent of small talk among them. It is such manifestations of nature as these on ground which is in one's stewardship that pulls at the heart-strings when the time comes for moving on and giving into other hands. How could we just sell our bit of Tanera to the highest bidder and think no more of the living things which are presently safe on its surface?

We did not spread slag very close to the cliff edge on Cnoc Ghlas, for we intended to fence it off as an insurance against the cattle going over and to allow the cliff to become a sanctuary and grow as it would. Nevertheless, a little of it went on ground which would not be grazed again and produced a strong growth here and there of grasses and clover. This untouched herbage provided the right conditions for the caterpillars of butterflies to feed, and their pupae were not disturbed by licking, garnering tongues, as they hung from stems and leaves. A whole book could be written on the ecology of grazing, for apart from its agricultural significance, the influence of grazing on wild life is profound. Three years ago we would have been exercised to find primrose plants along that cliff edge and even milkwort and dog-violets showed no luxuriance of growth. Now they are there in profusion, and being the food plants of the dark green fritillary and the pearl-bordered fritillary, do in fact go to nourish the caterpillars of these beautiful butterflies. I love now to take my siesta lying in the long herbage of the cliff on a hot afternoon of July. The swift-flying chequered forms of the fritillaries flash here and there, meadow browns pass more soberly, and innumerable common blues rest like sapphires in the grass. To have seen one of these three years ago would have been remarkable, and here they are in plenty, adding to the glory of the island summer.

The influence of basic slag on the arable ground is not so spectacular as on pasture, but its effects are obvious to the enquiring mind. We have used it heavily on the garden ground and given all of fifteen hundredweights to the acre to each piece of the park as we ploughed it. Phosphates are particularly needed by the plant after germination and for making early root growth. It is usual to experience a drought on the West Highland coastal strip between April and June, a drought which must be considered not only as a time of no rain but of extremely rapid evaporation of soil water through the light east and north winds and hot sunlight. If garden plants have weak roots at that time they wilt and die, and even should they survive they do not recover their full thrust of growth. The use of phosphate in the garden, therefore, is doubly necessary; in a countryside which buys all its cabbage plants and the like, we have been able to grow enough and to spare, plants with extraordinarily good root development which take hold in their new quarters without set-back.

Farming the arable ground of a croft to advantage calls for a searching questioning of one's ideas on farming and a readiness to put the traditional on one side. Assuming that we have got the ground into good heart by liming, mucking and slagging, what policy is then obvious in face of the limited area of arable land and the fact of the mild climate? In an area of cheap land we are apt to forget that this small amount of arable ground is valuable; on its cultivation must rest the ability of the croft and the countryside to *winter* stock, to winter a cattle stock which will approach in numbers the high summer potential of the hill grazings. The answer is intensification. The extensive grazing system of the rough ground will remain ranch-like, but we should treat the small areas of arable land like a garden and not cultivate it on the rough-and-ready methods of the farm.

Thus, when we began work on the garden which was to help feed cattle as well as ourselves we were not satisfied with plain digging of a dirty turf. We trenched every bit of new ground and took off an initial crop of potatoes which called for movement of the soil in hoeing and earthing-up while the crop was growing. The coastal croft is in the fortunate position of having a plentiful supply of potash-rich manure to hand in the shape of seaweed. It also contains nitrogen, but is deficient in phosphates. The use of seaweed has greatly declined and seaware is blamed by the crofters because it "forces" the ground. What they mean, but cannot explain, is that continual use of seaweed unbalances the soil. If adequate lime and phosphates are given, seaweed is a valuable source of additional fertility. As we trenched our ground we put a layer of seaweed at the bottom of each trench to help rot the turf of the next row, which was then inverted on it. We have also carried much seaweed to the manure heap and mixed it layer for layer with the dung.

Digging the potatoes in autumn means that the ground gets another working. Swedes are grown in the following year, the ground being deeply worked and heavily manured with the dung and seaweed compost. A further dressing of basic slag is given for this crop and the liming of the land is done now rather than when it was first trenched for potatoes. Swedes are but little grown in the North-West Highlands now because they need phosphates and lime more than do common turnips. But if they are properly fed there is nothing in the climate to prevent their being grown; they are much preferable to the turnip in being of higher feeding value and they keep better at the end of the winter.

We also grow cabbage and giant curly kale on either the first- or second-year ground. The curly kale is best sown in August in a sheltered place and transplanted in April. It is then in production from August onwards when the natural pastures are beginning to fail the cows. Its stumps may be cleared by October, but new growth continues during the winter and there is another good crop of green food in April and May when the man with cows is particularly glad of it. Curly kale is much preferable to any other kind as its leaves are highly resistant to wind. We do grow some of the ordinary drumhead cow cabbage for early use, but our main crop is composed of blue pickling cabbages and savoys. The latter come in about Christmas and New Year time and are wind-resistant; the blue cabbages are grown because of their intense closeness of growth which makes them good keepers—and again they resist wind and weather exceptionally well. I have read that before the swede turnip was introduced into this country in the eighteenth century the blue cabbage was the winter stand-by of the Aberdeenshire cattle-breeders, and Aberdeenshire weather is much harder than ours. The blue cabbages are particularly sweet and nothing we grow is more relished by the cows.

After the second year the garden ground is thoroughly made, clean and in good heart. We have not yet put a straw crop on any of it but are keeping it running on garden lines though the crop grown may be for the cows.

Both farmer and crofter find the spring sowing season a time of stress because so many things have to be done at once.

Working the land and manuring it for the root crop is particularly a job which causes rush. We set out to spread the root crops over at least a month of time because a crofter is usually single-handed and has no up-to-date machinery for saving labour. Could we spread the work by growing different crops requiring different sowing times? Turnips or swedes are not the beginning or end of a farmer's root crops. The technique we have developed here is to divide the root ground into three: one third is highly cultivated land manured the previous year and dug in winter; it is in such good fettle that it breaks down to a fine tilth easily in the dry weather of March. At the end of that month or in the first week of April we sow it with carrots in rows fifteen inches apart. Thus, a third of the root crop is sown with little more than a day or two's work. After-cultivation is done on garden lines and the singling at two intervals during the summer provides a cash crop of young carrots. Red carrots have a higher nutritive content than either swedes or mangolds and have the added virtue of containing three times as much carotene (the precursor of Vitamin A) as good pasture grass. Swedes and mangolds have practically none. The average field crop of carrots is twelve to fifteen tons to the acre, but by intensive cultivation on garden lines we have lifted a crop which has yielded at the rate of thirty tons to the acre. Apart from the higher food value, this is actually a heavier tonnage than we have got so far from swedes. The carrot fly has not yet come to Tanera!

We then considered the mangold as a crofter's root crop. It has become the main root crop of the South and Midlands of England but is not generally grown in Scotland except in the dairying districts of Galloway. But what do we really mean by dismissing the mangold as a crop which cannot be successfully grown in the North? We are quite right in saying it is no good if we have in mind poor soil, little manure and upland conditions—common turnips are the crop for such land. The mangold is descended from the wild sea beet, a plant found within the spray line and never far inland. Salt is a manure often applied to mangolds in inland districts. And this plant must have high feeding and be saved from frost. There seemed no good reason for not trying it on Tanera, except that our high

August rainfall and lack of sun in that month might cause an undue proportion of the plants to bolt to seed.

Our first mangolds were grown in 1942, using a heavy dressing of farmyard manure and seaweed only and no artificials. It was the most sunless year we have ever known and the rain fell four days out of five from the beginning of June till November. The mangolds could not have had a worse trial year, but the red intermediate variety yielded at the rate of forty-five tons to the acre, which is equal to the best English yields. This crop is sown at the end of April and lifted in November. The mangold tops may be fed to the cows at that time and form a welcome saving of the cabbages. Mangolds are certainly a crofter's crop if he will do them well enough.

Swedes are sown in May, and on this coastal strip it is unnecessary to lift them in the autumn. We get a crop of about twenty-five tons to the acre—which is not good enough on intensive lines—which we begin to feed about 10th January, the supply being pulled fresh each day. The roots have still a fair amount of green tops which is a welcome bite for the cows. We are also able to leave the carrots in the ground in this climate, and dig them as we need them. Thus the animals get them in the best possible condition of juiciness. Mangolds and carrots are fed mixed, in the late winter and early spring after the swedes are finished.

It is not unduly paradoxical to say that cows and a garden go well together as long as they are kept strictly apart! The good garden must have plenty of muck and there is little in the way of garden surplus which a cow cannot use economically—all surplus cabbagey things from the seed-bed, finished sprout plants in spring, pea haulms at the end of summer and so on. These things would be inconsiderable on a large farm but not so on a croft which is aiming at a winter milk supply from, say, two cows, and rearing a heifer calf or two at the same time.

Another garden crop which has been highly successful on Tanera is cauliflower. The heads have been superbly close and white and very large. Spring broccoli has also done well, and winter broccoli not so well, for wind and rain spoil the heads. This great asset of mildness, to which may be added the high total of daylight in early summer, allows us to get garden crops going early. We have now taken to the use of small tent cloches for starting some seeds such as lettuce and onions. The lettuce is getting its first pulling about the middle of May. Onion thinnings are being used all summer, and then early in September the cloches come out again to cover the onions to help dry and ripen them.

I am not one of those who say that a development of the tourist industry must be the main hope of prosperity in the Highlands, but I do say that there will be an inevitable increase in the number of tourists in the future. For the West Highlander to live off the proceeds of taking in lodgers would degrade him, I am afraid, because he is as yet too near the primitive style of life in tradition. He can, nevertheless, take positive steps to feed the visitors his wife may be housing, with a gain in self-respect.

It is the constant complaint of visitors to the Highlands that fresh food is hard to get. Fruit and vegetables, when obtainable, have been bumped over the roads from the East and South in a lorry, milk is growing scarce by August, home-made butter is scarce and usually of poor quality, and skim-milk products do not rise above crowdy.

I can see little hope of an export market for the fruit and vegetables which the coastal crofting strip could grow in such profusion, for communications are too slow at present. But there is this important seasonal population of tourists to be fed, and what is still more important, there is the crofter's own household to be adequately nourished for twelve months of the year. The number of bad teeth and "sair stomichs" and the all-too-common lack of energy are proof that nutrition is not adequate.

The milk problem is acute, and as I see it the Department of Agriculture for Scotland has not taken a long-sighted view of the situation in placing Aberdeen-Angus bulls in West Highland crofting townships. These cattle are too good for the Western grazings—by which I mean the grazings and standard of winter keep are not good enough for them. The usual thing is for the cows, now mostly black-polled and possibly three-parts Aberdeen-Angus, to calve in February or March. The black calves are much sought after in the markets of Dingwall, Inverness and Oban for rearing. The crofter may get £7 for his calf instead of the £3 he would have got a few years ago for a cross-Highland or nondescript calf. This is good going until October comes and the cow goes dry, and thereafter until February or March the crofter's family is living on condensed milk at 8½d. a tin. In the interests of the West Highlands as a nursery of men we must get home-produced winter milk into the townships.

The condition of the grassland and arable ground in the Highlands is poor. The consequences of shortage of lime and phosphates and of the social depression have been a discontinuance of ploughing and a decline in the number of cattle. In order to raise the number of milk cows fed largely from the produce of the croft we must get the plough going on these rushy parks. It is hard work. My Trusty tractor should plough over an acre a day on good ground, but when breaking the park from rushes, some heather and willow scrub, and moving glacial boulders, I have often done no more than a quarter of an acre a day. The physical strength needed for working the tractor in such conditions is all a man can exert. I have seen myself come in almost done at lunch-time and after the meal fall off to sleep solidly for an hour; then I could go on till nightfall. The human frame needs more than shop bread and tea to back it for this kind of work.

I am an admirer of Sir George Stapledon's system of increasing the fertility of grasslands by the use of the plough and taking several short leys. Some modification is necessary, though, for Highland conditions because much of this ground when newly turned up cannot be worked at all. The furrow slices are like slabs of rubber and just as bouncy; to put a set of harrows on such stuff means either an accident or at best the thinner furrow slices are caught up and make a piece of earthy swiss roll. The cultivator is no good because it exposes the turf again, which is exactly what you are trying to prevent. I found the best plan was to get the ploughing done, sow the slag and lime, then invert the harrows and run them over the ground a few times to rub a little soil between the furrow slices. A grass ley is not sown, but a crop of oats of one of the varieties suited to this part and which have a higher forage value than the newer kinds one would sow on better land. I used Sandy and Bell oats, but I might have used the Potato oat or Tam Finlay. All these give a nutritious straw. The grain is broadcast but slips into the junctions of the furrow slices and grows in distinct rows. Half a dozen harrowings with inverted harrows produce some tilth, and then the piece is rolled and gets no more cultivation until the crop is taken off. It is possible to give the ground a more thorough working in the following spring and sow it down to a short grass ley. The rubberiness is gone by that time. Some of the oats on the ground we turned grew to seven feet high, the leaves being as much as one and a half inches across. The crop went down, of course, in the bad gales and rain of August, but these oats seem able to stand a good deal of ill treatment and yet make up into a fresh and relished sheaf. That ground we ploughed which had not been turned within living memory grew a heavy and even crop of oats remarkably free from weeds. That which had last been ploughed in 1917 grew the strongest and heaviest crop but was dirty with wild mustard and stachys.

Oats should remain a standard crop for the crofter, for they will stand a good deal of bad weather and yield a lot of forage. But to turn grass into hay is more doubtful as a policy. It is no exaggeration to say that 50 per cent. of the nutritive value of the hay crop in the West Highlands is lost each year because of the heavy rain in late July and August. When haymaking is postponed till September there is still a fair chance of bad weather spoiling it, the sun has lost its drying power and the herbage itself is of poorer value at that time. There are two courses open by cutting out meadow hay altogether and growing short leys of Italian and perennial rye grass and red and Alsike clover. These courses are to push the crop in April with a dressing of one-and-a-half hundredweights of nitrate of lime to the acre so that it is ready to cut early in June, or to make silage. June is usually a dry month in the Highlands and the drying power of the weather is extraordinary on the coastal strip. Hay can be made then with a minimum of labour in both cutting and working. It is not possible to take this course if the bad habit has been indulged of keeping the ewes and lambs on the grass parks till the end of May! If a hay crop has been taken in June, another nitrate dressing of three-quarters of a hundred-weight to the acre will help the grass along again for a cut in late summer or autumn. It may be ensiled, used for weaning lambs or cut green each day as a soiling crop for the cows. This last is what I have done myself, but I admit that after the flattening effect of October's gales it is very hard work cutting the aftermath, and in rainy weather it is heavy and awkward to carry. Nevertheless, the cows milk well on it, and dry fodder is being saved. These tactics of giant short leys and two dressings of nitrate in the year are sheer suicide unless the land has been well limed and slagged and got into good heart, but if that has been done there is nothing in the climate to prevent enormous crops of grass and clover being grown. The practice of making grass and clover mixtures into silage has been reduced to a much surer process in recent years, and the cost of silos is now low. Ensiling two cuts a year of grass mixture means there is no loss from weathering and the winter stock-carrying capacity of the croft has been raised. Manure is more plentiful the next year and more ground can be the better cultivated.

For example, the extra manure could go to growing a crop of early potatoes. The tubers of such varieties as Duke of York or Arran Pilot should be sprouted in January and February and planted in early March. By this means we have been digging the potatoes by 20th June each year, and by July the crop has been heavy. Those we have not used or sold we have let run on as a main crop and got a very heavy yield. It is our experience that early potatoes miss the blight (which ruined our main crop in 1942) and that the tubers keep into the following spring just as well as the main crops. Duke of Yorks are particularly good for keeping.

There remains the question of what kind of cattle are best to keep if the stock is to be increased and winter milk made available. I think it would be inadvisable to go in whole-heartedly for a dairy breed, because the export of young grazing stock is a natural way of utilizing the rough grazings. A black- or blue-polled, weaned calf at five or six months old is worth about £12, which shows a better profit than rearing a dairy shorthorn bullock to that age or selling Ayrshire bull calves for veal at a fortnight old. It is my belief that there are many black- and blue-polled cows in the Highlands now which would milk well if properly fed. My own cows, for which I have gone no farther than Achiltibuie, have given records of 845 gallons and 650 gallons (twice) in twelve months on war-time feeding, and I have had the type of bull calf to sell which fetches high prices. The habit of milk recording should be encouraged and selection made among the cattle at present in the Highlands. Certain strains of Galloway cattle are remarkable for their milking qualities although as a breed they are noted as beef producers and as rough grazers. Bulls of such strains might be used in the townships in preference to the Aberdeen-Angus bulls used now.

It will need education to get the West Highlander into the way of being dairy-minded, for at present he considers work with cows to be derogatory to masculine dignity. "I have never milked a cow dry in my life", said an old man proudly to me one day. Another man told me it was too much trouble to grow swedes for a cow. Education will also be needed before garden produce can take its full place on the crofter's table. The standard of cookery in the Highlands is very low—and even if it were better in intention, it might be difficult immediately to better it in practice, for few crofters' homes have good ovens. Cookery means boiling or frying, both of which processes are apt to be killing to the food and hard on the stomach if carried to excess. I have even seen a gift of a brace of pheasants put into the boiling-pot with potatoes and cabbage! There is no baking of home-made bread leavened with yeast in the Highlands. Soda loaves are bad feeding, and girdle scones— nice as they are when fresh—are indigestible if eaten regularly instead of bread.

Bobbie and I feel that the standard of the crofter's table can be a high one. Here are all these fresh foods—milk, butter, eggs, fish, vegetables of innumerable kinds, all asking for simple but nevertheless careful cookery in order to supply a constant succession of appetizing dishes. We have to be vegetarians here by necessity rather than choice, but we rarely feel the urgent need of red meat. We look upon cookery as an art of life, and islanders, having few of the outside pleasures of civilization, should not disdain to make a point of getting all enjoyment possible out of their food.

As we see it, an uplifted West Highland crofting agriculture on distinctive lines would so raise the standard of living in the townships as to create a contentedness with life which would check the sense of defeatism which is no small part of the reason for the continued trend of depopulation.

Conclusion

THUS far have we come: what was a roofless ruin in 1939 is now a home where there is a fair standard of comfort. A good boat lies inside a safe quay. Those bare, rough acres which provided only a bite of summer grazing are now wintering six head of cattle from their own produce and so far feeding three people that their weekly outgoings for food do not amount to four shillings each a week in cash. There is also a surplus of produce to export from Tigh an Quay. The ground is fenced so that we can turn the cattle into different enclosures and rest content about them. We are clothed in tweed and knitted things made from the undyed moorit wool of our Shetland sheep. Not much money has been spent, but that which has gone into the place has been earned during the period of our work. The cost in the labour of our own bodies has been great, though I believe it has been a charge on the income of our strength and not on its capital. And we have not finished yet. We shall lose a few more finger-nails from getting them trapped between the big stones, and many another day shall we have to stop working with stone because the blood is showing pink through our finger-tips.

Perhaps we shall never finish Tigh an Quay and it will remain a road on which we have travelled hopefully. The place and our work on it have had their influence on the outside world, for good or ill. A wind-swept doom-ridden island property has begun to flower again and the principles we have used can be applied elsewhere. My own life here is on the point of enlarging and changing, in that the Department of Agriculture for Scotland has asked me to devote some of my time to travel in the crofting areas with a view to establishing demonstration crofts and advising crofters how to improve their holdings. For over three years Bobbie and I have worked alone, sometimes with discouraged monotony, sometimes with doubts as to whether it was worth while unless *the idea* went farther than Tigh an Quay, but usually with a deep enthusiasm. The advent of this new field of work, then, finds me grateful and a little ashamed for the moments of doubt. Doubt is a strange sin to me whose strength has ever been in faith; and I have known I have sinned when I have doubted.

I undertake this new work loving the folk for whom it will be done, loving them without illusion or sentiment. They will hurt and disappoint me as they have many a time already, but it does not matter. They also will warm my heart with kindly acts done with a beautiful simplicity which a more sophisticated society has lost. They are good folk and I have faith in them. The West will not be re-created for them from outside, but through them. If I had not this faith I could not go forward now to work with them. Had I begun it years ago I should have suffered disillusionment and perhaps fallen by the way. It is different today, for the disappointments will not be breaks in the walls of my personal citadel. The work is not my career, that thing which is the outward manifestation of personal ambition. Enthusiasm is there but the ego is out of it.

Bobbie and I set out to make this ruin of Tanera. It seemed to fight us for a while, two human beings attempting to clear a century of gathering doom; then we felt the weight lift, and though life held just as much hard work as before, life was easier a little. The island years on the Clerach, the Treshnish and Rona were a novitiate, but we *were* still novices in 1939. This book is a tale of what we have been doing to Tanera, a remote and unimportant island, but if the red stones and rough acres could talk they might tell another tale—of what Tanera has done to us.

ISLE OF TANERA
ROSS & CROMARTY
TIGH AN QUAY

G.C. LESLIE 43.

Cnoc an t-Sidhe.

The Park.

Tup Park.

SCALE   0   50   100   150   200   YARDS.